BASIC stress analysis

To

Helen, Emma and Simon

BASIC stress analysis

M J Iremonger
BSc (Eng), PhD, DIC, ACGI, CEng, MIMechE

Principal Lecturer
Royal Military College of Science, Shrivenham, England

Butterworth Scientific
London . Boston . Durban . Singapore . Sydney . Toronto . Welling

First published, 1982

©Butterworth & Co (Publishers) Ltd, 1982

British Library Cataloguing in Publication Data
Iremonger, M.J.
    BASIC stress analysis.
    1. Stress analysis – Data processing
    2. Basic (Computer program language)
    I. Title
    620. 1'123'028542   TA407

    ISBN 0-408-01113-0

Typeset by Scribe Design, Gillingham, Kent
Printed in England by Page Bros Ltd., Norwich, Norfolk

Preface

The importance of computers and computer programming has grown rapidly in recent years. This growth has been widespread and has been accelerated by the advent of microcomputers. Almost all engineers have, or will soon have, access to computer facilities and it is necessary that they see computing as a natural everyday tool.

Computing is in the curriculum of all university engineering courses and indeed it is often taught in schools. However, many students find it a difficult and alien subject, often because it is taught by computer scientists or mathematicians and not related to their engineering subjects. There are a number of advantages that can accrue from linking the study of engineering and computing. Engineering can help computing by showing its relevance and by providing exercises with which programming techniques can be learned, practised and developed. Computing is then seen as both an essential and natural activity for engineers. Computing can help engineering because a clear exposition (and consequent understanding) of the engineering equations and procedures is required in order to write a successful computer program. This approach can lead to an enthusiastic acceptance of computing. It is of value not only to student engineers but also to practising engineers who may not have been taught computing or who were perhaps 'scarred for life' by their experiences.

This book uses BASIC, a programming language which is often criticised by computer scientists because of its unstructured nature. For engineers BASIC has many advantages in addition to its widespread availability as a built-in microcomputer language. Its use of simple English statements makes it easy to learn and remember so that an engineer can surmount the initial hurdle of computing and then employ it usefully at infrequent intervals afterwards. BASIC programs can be rapidly developed because special compiling, linking and editing routines are not required — a help to both beginner and expert. Moreover, it allows a student to complete a programming exercise within a short period of time (e.g. an afternoon or study period) and thereby retains his interest and confidence in computing.

BASIC stress analysis has been written with this philosophy in mind. It aims to help students to become proficient at BASIC programming by actually using it in an important engineering subject. In addition it enables the student to use computing as a means of learning stress analysis because writing a program is analogous to teaching — it is necessary to understand the subject matter. The large number of short programs contained in this book should convince the most reluctant engineer of the ease and value of computing.

Chapter 1 is an introduction to BASIC. Chapter 2 introduces stress analysis at first- and second-year undergraduate level. Chapters 3 to 8 follow a sequence dictated by their stress analysis content. Each contains a summary of relevant theory, worked examples containing computer programs and a set of problems. The theory content may be useful as a 'revision note' synopsis of the subject though it is by no means comprehensive. The worked examples are posed as questions. A listing of a possible program is given followed by an example of its output and some 'Program Notes'. These notes explain the structure of the program and how it utilises the stress analysis theory. The programs require only limited computer storage capacity. The problems involve modifying or extending the example programs and writing completely new programs. The reader can learn about both BASIC programming and stress analysis by studying the examples and attempting the problems. The problems are not formally graded in difficulty but the first two in each of the Chapters 3 to 5 need little expertise.

Acknowledgement is due to a number of people including students at the Royal Military College of Science who have been exposed to my philosophy with (I hope) beneficial results. Credit is due to Professor Gordon Wood who has been a most enthusiastic convert to the cause, to Chris Prowting who has been instrumental in maintaining computer facilities of a high standard and to my colleague Peter Smith who has provided many ideas as a fellow author and editor. My thanks are particularly due to Mrs Kathleen Hunt who most ably typed the manuscript and to my wife Helen and daughter Emma without whose forbearance this work would not have been completed.

Michael John Iremonger

Contents

Principal stress analysis notation

			Basic units*
x, y		Cartesian co-ordinates	m, m
r, θ		Polar co-ordinates	m, rad
σ	(sigma)	Direct stress	)
σ_1, σ_2		Principal stresses	) N/m^2
σ_Y		Yield stress	)
ϵ	(epsilon)	Direct strain	
τ	(tau)	Shear stress	
γ	(gamma)	Shear strain	
E		Young's modulus (modulus of elasticity)	) N/m^2
G		Shear modulus (modulus of rigidity)	)
ν	(nu)	Poisson's ratio	
α	(alpha)	Linear coefficient of thermal expansion	/°C
P		Direct (tensile or compressive) force	N
p		Internal pressure	N/m^2
M		Bending moment	Nm
Q		Shear force	N
W		Concentrated (point) load	N
w		Uniformly distributed load per unit length	N/m
$L, 1$		Length	m
b, B		Breadth	m
d, D		Depth	m
t		Thickness	m
A		Area	m^2
R, r		Radius, radius of curvature	m
D, d		Diameter	m
I		Second moment of area	m^4
J		Polar second moment of area	m^4
δ	(delta)	Displacement (deflection)	m

*Note: in this book, mm is preferred to m as a unit of length.
Prefixes: k = 10^3 (e.g. 1 kN = 1000 N), $M = 10^6$, $G = 10^9$.

Chapter 1

Introduction to BASIC

1.1 The BASIC approach

The programs in this book are written in the BASIC programming
language. BASIC, an acronym for Beginner's All-purpose Symbolic
Instruction Code, was developed at Dartmouth College, USA as an easy-
to-learn, general-purpose language. Originally intended for use on time-
sharing computer systems, it has gained widespread popularity as the
main language associated with microcomputers. Not only is the
language easy to learn but it is also particularly easy to use. Without
complication a program can be written, typed in at the computer, run
and corrected and run again if any errors are present. The main dis-
advantages of simple BASIC relate to its lack of structure (see Section
1.4) but this is not an important consideration for short programs such
as those in the following chapters.

This book aims to help in the learning of BASIC by applying it to a
relevant engineering subject. This aim can be met by the reader
studying the examples, possibly copying them and then trying some of
the problems. Although this book does not specifically teach the
grammar of BASIC, a short description of the simple BASIC used is
given in the next section.

1.2 The elements of BASIC

1.2.1 *Mathematical expressions*

One of the main objects of the example programs in this book is to
evaluate the equations that arise in stress analysis. These equations
contain numerical constants, variables (e.g. x) and functions (e.g. sine).
All numbers are treated identically whether they are integer (e.g. 36)
or real (e.g. 36.1). An exponential form is used to represent large or
small numbers (e.g. 3.61E6 which equals 3.61×10^6). Numeric
variables are represented by a letter or a letter followed by a digit
(e.g. E or E1). On many computers π is directly available to the user
either as PI or as a π key. For generality π is always written as 3.14159
in the examples in this book. An operation, such as square root, can be

1

done using an in-built function (e.g. SQR (X)). The argument in brackets (X) can be a number, a variable or a mathematical expression. For trigonometric functions (SIN(X), COS (X), etc.) the argument is interpreted as being measured in radians. Other functions include a natural logarithm and its exponential (LOG and EXP respectively), ABS which selects the absolute value of argument and INT which selects the integer part of the argument.

Mathematical equations also contain operators such as plus and minus, etc. These operators have a hierarchy in that some are performed by the computer before others. In descending order of hierarchy the operators are

to the power of $(\wedge)$
multiply (*) and divide (/)
add (+) and subtract (−).

Thus, for example, multiplication is done before addition. The computer works from left to right if the operators have the same hierarchy. Brackets can be used to override any of these operations. Hence $\dfrac{a+b}{3c}$ becomes $(A + B)/(3*C)$ or $(A + B)/3/C$.

1.2.2 *Program structure and assignment*

A BASIC program is a sequence of statements which define a procedure for the computer to follow. As it follows this procedure the computer allocates values to each of the variables. The values of some of these variables may be specified by data that is input to the program. Others are generated in the program using, for instance, the assignment statement. This has the form

line number [LET] variable = mathematical expression

where the word LET is usually optional and therefore omitted. For example the root of a quadratic equation

$$x_1 = \frac{-b + \sqrt{(b^2 - 4ac)}}{2a}$$

may be obtained from a statement such as

100 X1 = (−B + SQR (B^2 − 4*A*C)) / (2*A)

It is important to realise that an assignment statement is not itself an equation. It is an instruction to give the variable on the left-hand side the numeric value of the expression on the right-hand side. Thus it is possible to have a statement

50 X = X + 1

which increases by 1 the value of X.

Each variable can have only one value at any time unless it is subscripted (see Section 1.2.7).

Note that all BASIC statements (i.e. all the program lines) are numbered. This defines the order in which they are executed.

1.2.3 *Input*

For 'interactive conversational' programs the user specifies variables by 'run-time' input of their values. The statement has the form

line number INPUT variable 1 [, variable 2, . . .]

e.g.

20 INPUT A, B, C

When the program is run the computer prints ? as it reaches this statement and waits for the user to type values for the variables, e.g.

? 5, 10, 15

which makes A = 5, B = 10 and C = 15 in the above example.

An alternative form of data input is useful if there are many data or if the data are not to be changed by the user (e.g. a range of available sizes as in Example 3.3). For this type of data specification there is a statement of the form

line number READ variable 1 [, variable 2, . . .]

e.g.

20 READ A, B, C

with an associated statement (or number of statements) of the form

line number DATA number 1 [, number 2, . . .]

e.g.

1 DATA 5, 10, 15

or

1 DATA 5
2 DATA 10
3 DATA 15

DATA statements can be placed anywhere in a program — it is often convenient to place them at the beginning so they can be easily changed (see Example 3.2).

When using built-in data it is sometimes necessary to read the data from their start more than once during a single program run (as in Example 3.3). This is done using the statement

line number RESTORE

1.2.4 *Output*

Output of data and the results of calculations, etc. is done using a statement of the form

line number PRINT list

The list may contain variables or expressions, e.g.

200 PRINT A, B, C, A*B/C

text enclosed in quotes, e.g.

10 PRINT 'INPUT A, B, C IN MM';

or mixed text and variables, e.g.

300 PRINT "STRESS IS"; S; "N/MM$^\wedge$2"

The items in the list are separated by commas or semi-colons. Commas give tabulation in columns, each about 15 spaces wide. A semi-colon suppresses this spacing and if it is placed at the end of a list it suppresses the line feed. If the list is left unfilled a blank line is printed.

Note the necessity to use PRINT statements in association with both 'run-time' input (to indicate what input is required) and READ/ DATA statements (because otherwise the program user has no record of the data).

1.2.5 *Conditional statements*

It is often necessary to enable a program to take some action if, and only if, some condition is fulfilled. This is done with a statement of the form

line number IF expression 1 $\begin{matrix} \text{conditional} \\ \text{operator} \end{matrix}$ expression 2 THEN line number

where the possible conditional operators are

```
=     equals
<>    not equal to
<     less than
<=    less than or equal to
>     greater than
>=    greater or equal to
```

For example a program could contain the following statements if it is to stop when a zero value of A is input, i.e.

```
20  INPUT A
30  IF A <> 0 THEN 50
40  STOP
50  ...
```

Note the statement

line number STOP

which stops the run of a program.

1.2.6 Loops

There are several means by which a program can repeat some of its procedure; the self-repeating sequence of program statement is called a loop. The simplest such statement is

line number GO TO line number

This can be used, for instance, with the above conditional statement example so that the program continues to request values of A until the user inputs zero.

The most common means of performing loops is with a starting statement of the form

line number FOR variable = expression 1 TO expression 2 [STEP expression 3]

where the STEP is assumed to be unity if omitted. The finish of the loop is signified by a statement

line number NEXT variable

where the same variable is used in both FOR and NEXT statements. Its value should not be changed in the intervening lines.

A loop is used if, for example, N sets of data have to be READ and their reciprocals printed, e.g.

```
10 READ N
20 PRINT "NUMBER", "RECIPROCAL"
30 FOR I = 1 To N
40 READ A
50 PRINT A, 1/A
60 NEXT I
```

Loops can also be used to generate data. Consider, for example, a simple temperature conversion program

```
10 PRINT "CENTIGRADE", "FAHRENHEIT"
20 FOR C = 0 TO 100 STEP 5
30 PRINT C, 9 * C/5 + 32
40 NEXT C
```

1.2.7 *Subscripted variables*

It is sometimes very beneficial to allow a single variable to have a number of different values during a single program run (see Examples 3.5, 4.6 and 5.6). For instance, if a program contains data for several materials it is convenient for their densities to be called $R(1)$, $R(2)$, $R(3)$, etc. instead of R1, R2, R3, etc. It is then possible for a single statement to perform calculations for all the materials, e.g.

```
50 FOR I = 1 TO N
60 M(I) = V * R(I)
70 NEXT I
```

which determines the mass $M(I)$ for each material from the volume (V) of the body.

A non-subscripted variable has a single value associated with it and if a subscripted variable is used it is necessary to provide space for all the values. This is done with a dimensioning statement of the form.

line number DIM variable 1 (integer 1) [, variable 2 (integer 2), . . .]

e.g.

```
20 DIM R(50), M(50)
```

which allows up to 50 values of R and M. The DIM statement must occur before the subscripted variables are first used.

On some computers it is possible to use a dimension statement of a different form, e.g.

20 DIM R(N), M(N)

where the value of N has been previously defined. This form, when available, has the advantage of not wasting space.

1.2.8 Subroutines

Sometimes a sequence of statements needs to be accessed more than once in the same program (see Example 3.5). Instead of merely repeating these statements it is better to put them in a subroutine. The program then contains statements of the form

line number GOSUB line number

When the program reaches this statement it branches (i.e. transfers control) to the second line number. The sequence of statements starting with this second line number ends with a statement

line number RETURN

and the program returns control to the statement immediately after the GOSUB call.

Subroutines can be placed anywhere in the program but it is usually convenient to position them at the end, separate from the main program statements.

Another reason for using a subroutine occurs when a procedure is written which is required in more than one program (see Examples 3.3 and 4.5). It is often desirable to use less common variable names (e.g. X9 instead of X) in such subroutines. This minimises the possibility of the same variable name being used with a different meaning in separate parts of a program.

1.2.9 Other statements

(1) Explanatory remarks or headings which are not to be output can be inserted into a program using

line number REM comment

Any statement beginning with the word REM is ignored by the computer. On some computers it is possible to include remarks on the same line as other statements (see Example 6.2).

(2) Non-numeric data (e.g. words) can be handled by string variables. A string is a series of characters within quotes, e.g. 'STRESS' and a

string variable is a letter followed by a $ sign, e.g. S$. They are particularly valuable when printed headings need to be varied (see Example 3.5).

(3) Multiple branching can be done with statements of the form

line number ON expression THEN line number 1 [, line number 2, . . .]

and

line number ON expression GOSUB line number 1 [, line number 2, . . .]

When a program reaches one of these statements it branches to line number 1 if the integer value of the expression is 1, to line number 2 if the expression is 2, and so on. An error message is printed if the expression gives a value less than 1 or greater than the number of referenced line numbers. The programs in Examples 7.5 and 7.6 contain examples of the ON . . . GOSUB and the ON . . . THEN statements respectively.

(4) Functions other than those built into the language such as SIN(X) can be created as defined functions using a DEF statement. For example

10 DEF FNA(X) = X^3 + X^2 + X + 1

defines a cubic function which can be recalled later in the program as FNA (variable) where the value of this variable is substituted for X. A defined function is useful if an algebraic expression is to be evaluated several times in a program (see Example 5.6).

1.3 Checking programs

Most computers give a clear indication if there are grammatical (syntax) errors in a BASIC program. Program statements can be modified by retyping them correctly or by using special editing procedures. The majority of syntax errors are easy to locate but if a variable has been used with two (or more) different meanings in separate parts of the program some mystifying errors can result.

It is not sufficient for the program to be just grammatically correct. It must give the correct answers. A program should therefore be checked either by using data which give a known solution or by hand calculation. If the program is to be used with a wide range of data or by users other than the program writer, it is necessary to check that all parts of it function. It is also important to ensure that the program does not give incorrect but plausible answers when 'nonsense' data is input. It is quite difficult to make programs completely 'userproof' and they become lengthy in so doing. The programs in this book have been kept as short as possible for the purpose of clarity and may not therefore be fully 'userproof'

1.4 Different computers and variants of BASIC

The examples in this book use a simple version of BASIC that should work on most computers, even those with small storage capacity. Only single-line statements have been used though many computers allow a number of statements on each line with a separator such as \. Multiple assignments may also be possible so that, for instance, the program in Example 4.6 could be simplified by replacing lines 1040 to 1080 with a single statement such as

> 1040 S1 = S2 = S3 = S4 = S5 = 0

There is one important feature which distinguishes computers, particularly microcomputers, with a visual display unit (VDU). This concerns the number of available columns across each line and the number of rows that are visible on the screen. Simple modifications of some of the programs may be necessary to fit the output to a particular microcomputer. TAB printing is a useful facility for this purpose.

Various enhancements to BASIC have been made since its inception and these are implemented on a number of computer systems. The programs in this book could be re-written to take account of some of these 'advanced' features. For example, the ability to use long variable names (e.g. STRESS instead of, say, S or S1) makes it easier to write unambiguous programs. Other advanced facilities include more powerful looping and conditional statements and independent sub-routines which make the writing of structured programs easier. In simplistic terms, structured programming involves the compartmentalisation of programs and minimises branching due to statements containing 'GO TO line number' and 'THEN line number'. Good program structure is advantageous for long programs.

1.5 Summary of BASIC statements

Assignment

LET	Computes and assigns value
DIM	Allocates space for subscripted variables

Input

INPUT	'Run-time' input of data
READ	Reads data from DATA statements
DATA	Storage area for data
RESTORE	Restores DATA to its start

Output
PRINT	Prints output

Program control
STOP	Stops program run
GO TO	Unconditional branching
IF . . . THEN	Conditional branching
FOR. . .TO. .STEP	Opens loop
NEXT	Closes loop
GOSUB	Transfers control to subroutine
RETURN	Returns control from subroutine
ON. . .THEN	Multiple branching
ON. . .GOSUB	Multiple subroutine transfer

Comment
REM	Comment in program

Functions
SQR	Square root
SIN	Sine (angle in radians)
COS	Cosine (angle in radians)
ATN	Arctangent (gives angle in radians)
LOG	Natural logarithm (base e)
EXP	Exponential
ABS	Absolute value
INT	Integral value
DEF FN	Defined function

1.6 Bibliography

Alcock, D., *Illustrating BASIC*, Cambridge University Press, (1977).
Kemeny, J.G. and Kurtz, T.E., *BASIC Programming*, Wiley, (1968).
Monro, D.M., *Interactive Computing with BASIC,* Edward Arnold, (1974).

Chapter 2

Introduction to stress analysis

2.1 The nature of stress analysis

Stress analysis is concerned with the behaviour of bodies under load. It is sometimes called *Solid mechanics, Strength of materials* or *Mechanics of materials* because of the major role played by material behaviour.

Experimental stress analysis is an important practical tool but a theoretical approach is usual with computer techniques becoming increasingly common. Advanced theoretical treatments of the subject are based on the *theory of elasticity*.

Almost invariably stress analysis uses a *continuum* approach which assumes a material to be homogeneous and to behave in an 'average' way. The existence therefore of individual atoms, molecules and grain boundaries is largely ignored.

2.2 The aims of stress analysis

The primary objects of stress *analysis* are to determine internal stresses and strains within a component and thereby to answer the following questions, 'Will it break?', 'Will it deform too much?'

It is clearly desirable for these questions to be answered in the negative. The *design* process is therefore a reverse procedure which entails determining the dimensions of the component so that it will neither break nor deform too much.

2.3 The principles of stress analysis

The theoretical approach to stress analysis is based on three principles.

(1) *Equilibrium* of forces: the forces acting on a body must balance themselves in order that the body remains stationary. This applies to both the whole body and to any small or large part of the body. The forces may therefore be external or internal forces. Dynamic equilibrium conditions can be applied but most analyses are for static problems.

11

(2) *Compatibility* of displacements: different parts of a body must fit together and there are relationships between displacements in internal parts of the body – they must be compatible.

(3) *Stress-strain relation*: for any material there is an innate relationship between strain (i.e. displacement) and stress (i.e. internal force).

These three conditions or 'tools' of stress analysis enable equations to be written from which a problem can be solved. It is necessary, in addition, to take account of the boundary conditions for the problem, i.e. the forces and displacements at the component's boundaries.

Some problems require a joint consideration of equilibrium and compatibility in order to determine the external forces. Such a system is called *statically indeterminate*. Systems for which the forces can be found from equilibrium alone are called *statically determinate*.

2.4 Units

For the most part, stress analysis uses units of only force and length. The SI unit for force is a newton (N) and for length is a metre (m). It is common in stress analysis to use a millimetre (mm) length unit. This is because the dimensions of many components are most conveniently expressed in mm and because the units for stress can be N/mm^2. This use of N/mm^2 instead of N/m^2 is often preferred because it emphasises that a stress is a force acting over a small area. It has the additional advantage of producing more convenient numbers – stresses in metals are typically between 20 and 200 N/mm^2. Note that

$$1 \text{ N/mm}^2 = 10^6 \text{ N/m}^2 = 1 \text{ MN/m}^2$$

2.5 The scope of this book

The following chapters cover aspects of stress analysis taught in the first two years of an engineering degree course.

The chapters follow a logical sequence. Chapters 3 and 4 describe the determination of stress and strain in simple systems. Chapter 4 also covers torsion and Chapter 5 describes bending. These are systems for which the stress is not uniform. Chapter 6 deals with more complex situations in which different stresses are combined. The examples in these chapters embody the aims outlined in Section 2.2 from the points of view of both analysis and design. However the question 'Will it break?' is dealt with more fully in Chapter 7 which describes some of the more 'unexpected' forms of failure – brittle fracture, fatigue and buckling. Finally, Chapter 8 considers axisymmetric systems which include thick-walled cylinders, an example of more complex analysis.

Each chapter contains a summary of relevant theory and additional aspects are covered in some of the examples. It is important to note however that the coverage of each topic is far from complete and that, in the limited space available, many details are omitted. Each of the references at the end of this chapter covers most of the 'theory' content of this book in considerably more detail. The reader should refer to them or to similar works when not familiar with the theory. Reference [7] is not a general book on stress analysis; it describes in detail the application of fracture mechanics to static brittle fracture and to fatigue crack growth (see Chapter 7). The other references make little mention of this subject.

2.6 References

[1] Muvdi, B.B. and McNabb, J.W., *Engineering Mechanics of Materials,* Macmillan, (1980).

[2] Popov, E.G., *Mechanics of Materials* 2nd ed., Prentice Hall, (1978).

[3] Ryder, G.H., *Strength of Materials* 3rd ed., MacMillan, (1969).

[4] Benham, P.P. and Warnock, F.V., *Mechanics of Solids and Structures*, Pitman, (1973).

[5] Megson, T.H.G., *Strength of Materials for Civil Engineers,* Nelson, (1980).

[6] Hearn, E.J., *Mechanics of Materials Vols 1 & 2,* Pergamon, (1977).

[7] Parker, A.P. *The Mechanics of Fracture and Fatigue,* Spon, (1981).

Chapter 3

Direct stress and strain

ESSENTIAL THEORY

3.1 Direct stress

Stress is a measure of the intensity of loading represented by force divided by the area over which the force acts. A stress component at right angles to the plane on which it acts is called a *direct stress* and is either *tensile* (+ve) or *compressive* (−ve). In the definition

$$\sigma = P/A \qquad (3.1)$$

σ represents the actual (uniform) stress if the force P is uniformly distributed over the area A and the average stress if P is not uniformly distributed. In the latter case the actual stress at any point can be defined by the limiting ratio of $\delta P/\delta A$ where δA represents the area of a small element of material over which the stress can be reasonably assumed to be uniform. The units for stress are N/m^2 or multiples of this such as MN/m^2 or N/mm^2.

3.2 Direct strain

Strain is a dimensionless form for representing deformation. A direct stress produces a *direct strain* ϵ given by

$$\epsilon = \delta/L \qquad (3.2)$$

where δ is the increase in an original length L. By this definition tensile strains (elongations) are positive and compressive strains (contractions) negative.

3.3 Stress-strain relationships

Stress and strain are related for any material (though this relationship may vary with temperature, rate of loading, etc.). Some typical tensile stress—strain curves are shown in Figure 3.1. For many materials and conditions the behaviour (for stresses below some critical level) fits Hooke's law which states that deformation is directly proportional to

14

the load producing it, i.e. stress is proportional to strain. The gradient 'direct stress divided by direct strain' is then a constant called *Young's modulus* (E, modulus of elasticity or elastic modulus*) given by

$$E = \sigma/\epsilon \tag{3.3}$$

The units for modulus are N/m^2 or multiples of this such as GN/m^2 or kN/mm^2. Associated with Hooke's law is the phenomenom called *elasticity* which means that when the stress is removed the strain returns to zero.

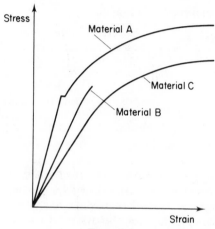

Figure 3.1

The behaviour of some materials is linearly elastic (i.e. Hooke's law is obeyed) until near to failure (material B in Figure 3.1). Such materials are termed *brittle*. Other materials suffer irrecoverable (plastic) deformation beyond a critical stress level (the *elastic limit*) at which they 'yield'. If the yield point (hence *yield strength*) is not sharply defined, yielding is represented by a *proof stress* (obtained from an offset to the linear stress–strain region as shown for material C in Figure 3.1). The maximum tensile stress carried by a material is called the *ultimate tensile strength*.

Materials which can undergo significant plastic deformation are termed *ductile*. The maximum allowable stress in a material (its *working* or *design* stress) is the yield, proof or tensile strength divided by a *safety factor*.

---

*The *stiffness* of a component is the load required for unit deformation. Stiffness is a function of elastic modulus and component geometry. For components of similar dimensions stiffness is directly proportional to modulus and the words stiffness and modulus are often used synonymously.

3.4 Poisson's ratio

When a bar is extended due to a tensile load it contracts in directions normal to the loading direction. Within the elastic limit the ratio of lateral compressive strain to axial tensile strain is a constant called *Poisson's ratio* (v). Hence an axial stress σ_x causes an axial strain $\epsilon_x = \sigma_x/E$, and a lateral strain $\epsilon_y = -v\epsilon_x$, where y represents a direction normal to x. The negative sign is introduced so that tensile strains are positive and compressive strains are negative.

3.5 Hooke's law in three dimensions

If there are stresses σ_x, σ_y and σ_z acting in three mutually perpendicular directions x, y and z, the Hooke's law relations can be written as

$$\epsilon_x = \frac{1}{E}\left[\sigma_x - v(\sigma_y + \sigma_z)\right]$$

$$\epsilon_y = \frac{1}{E}\left[\sigma_y - v(\sigma_z + \sigma_x)\right] \tag{3.4}$$

$$\epsilon_z = \frac{1}{E}\left[\sigma_z - v(\sigma_x + \sigma_y)\right]$$

These relationships are obtained using the *Principle of Superposition.* This holds for linear elastic material behaviour when the strains are small, which they are for most engineering problems. Equations (3.4) also assume *isotropic* material behaviour (i.e. the properties are independent of direction).

3.6 Strain energy

When a body is loaded the work done is stored as strain energy by the deformed material. Within the elastic limit this energy is recoverable and is represented by the area under the load-deflection curve. Using the terminology defined above, the strain energy (U) is given by

$$U = \frac{1}{2}P\delta \tag{3.5}$$

or in terms of strain energy per unit volume (U_v)

$$U_v = \frac{1}{2}\frac{P}{A}\frac{\delta}{L} = \frac{1}{2}\sigma\epsilon = \sigma^2/2E \tag{3.6}$$

The area under the stress–strain curve to failure is a measure of the work done (i.e. energy absorbed) in fracturing the material. As can be inferred from Figure 3.1 ductile materials can generally absorb more energy than brittle materials. This absorbed energy is a measure of *toughness*.

3.7 Temperature stresses

Temperature stresses arise when thermal expansion or contraction is constrained. A bar that is restrained at its ends and subjected to a uniform temperature increase T, develops along its length a compressive direct stress

$$\sigma = -E \alpha T \tag{3.7}$$

where α is the (linear) coefficient of thermal expansion. The product αT represents a 'temperature strain'.

3.8 Compound bars

An analysis which brings together much of the content of this chapter is that of compound bars. These are members comprising parallel bars or tubes made of two (or more) different materials. To analyse the tensile or compressive behaviour of such members when subjected to axial or thermal loading requires a joint consideration of both equilibrium and compatibility — the system is statically indeterminate.

Consider the two concentric tubes shown in Figure 3.2 which are made of two materials with elastic moduli E_1 and E_2 and cross-section areas A_1 and A_2 respectively.

If the tubes are fixed together at their ends and they are subjected to an axial tensile load P the direct stresses in the two materials (σ_1 and σ_2) are found from Equations (3.8) and (3.9) below.

The total load P is shared between the two tubes — equilibrium. Hence

$$P = \sigma_1 A_1 + \sigma_2 A_2 \tag{3.8}$$

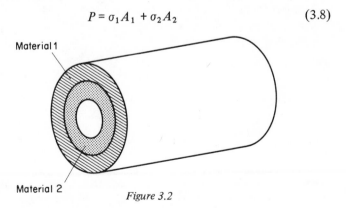

Material 1

Material 2

Figure 3.2

The tubes develop equal axial strains (ϵ) — compatibility. Hence

$$\epsilon = \sigma_1/E_1 = \sigma_2/E_2 \qquad (3.9)$$

If the concentric tubes shown in Figure 3.2 are subjected to a uniform temperature rise T, stresses will be developed if their coefficients of thermal expansion (α_1 and α_2 respectively) are different. As there is no resultant force on the member the equilibrium equation (3.8) holds with P equal to zero. The compatibility equation represents the equality of strain for each material. The strains consist of both temperature strains and stress-induced strains. Thus

$$\alpha_1 T + \sigma_1/E_1 = \alpha_2 T + \sigma_2/E_2 \qquad (3.10)$$

Hence the stresses σ_1 and σ_2 can be determined.

WORKED EXAMPLES

Example 3.1 Direct stress

Write a program to determine direct stress (in N/mm^2) from 'run-time' input of axial force (kN) and cross-section area (mm^2). The program should enable repeated calculations to be made but should stop if a zero value of axial force is input.

```
EX3POINT1   3-JUN-81   13:34:52

10 PRINT "DIRECT STRESS CALCULATION"
20 PRINT "----------------------------------"
30 PRINT
40 PRINT "INPUT:"
50 PRINT "AXIAL FORCE (KN) - 0 TO STOP";
60 INPUT P
70 P=P*1000
80 IF P<>0 THEN 100
90 STOP
100 PRINT "CROSS-SECTION AREA (MM^2)";
110 INPUT A
120 S=P/A
130 PRINT "DIRECT STRESS IS";S;"N/MM^2"
140 GO TO 30

READY
RUN

EX3POINT1   3-JUN-81   13:35:06

DIRECT STRESS CALCULATION
-----------------------------------------------

INPUT:
AXIAL FORCE (KN) - 0 TO STOP? 25
CROSS-SECTION AREA (MM^2)? 450
DIRECT STRESS IS 55.5556 N/MM^2

INPUT:
AXIAL FORCE (KN) - 0 TO STOP? 5
CROSS-SECTION AREA (MM^2)? 240
DIRECT STRESS IS 20.8333 N/MM^2
```

Example 3.2 Young's modulus from tensile tests   19

```
INPUT:
AXIAL FORCE (KN) - 0 TO STOP? 0

STOP AT LINE 90

READY
```

Program notes

(1) The stress S is evaluated in line 120 using Equation (3.1).
(2) Line 70 converts the input value of axial force into Newtons.
(3) The IF statement in line 80 causes the program to stop at line 90 when a zero value of axial force is input.

Example 3.2 Young's modulus from tensile tests

Tensile tests on a number of steel specimens give data for cross-section area, gauge length, tensile force and extension.

Write a program to determine values of Young's modulus (E) for each specimen and to find the average value of E for the whole sample with the corresponding standard deviation.

Test the program with the following data

Cross-section area – A (mm^2)	Gauge length – L (mm)	Force – P (kN)	Extension – X (mm)
78	50	6.68	0.021
80	50	7.49	0.023
77	50	5.85	0.019
79	25	7.31	0.011
78	25	7.86	0.012

```
EX3POINT2   3-JUN-81  14:05:32

1 DATA 5
2 DATA 78,50,6.68,.021
3 DATA 80,50,7.49,.023
4 DATA 77,50,5.85,.019
5 DATA 79,25,7.31,.011
6 DATA 78,25,7.86,.012
100 PRINT "ANALYSIS OF TENSION TESTS"
110 PRINT "----------------------------------"
120 PRINT
130 PRINT "AREA","LENGTH","FORCE","EXTENSION","MODULUS E"
140 PRINT "(MM^2)","  (MM)","(KN)","   (MM)","(KN/MM^2)"
150 S1=0
160 S2=0
170 READ N
180 FOR I=1 TO N
190 READ A,L,P,X
200 E=P*L/A/X
210 S1=S1+E
220 S2=S2+E*E
230 PRINT A,L,P,X,E
240 NEXT I
```

```
250 PRINT "AVERAGE VALUE OF E IS";S1/N;"KN/MM^2"
260 S5=SQR((N*S2-S1*S1)/(N*(N-1)))
270 PRINT "WITH A STANDARD DEVIATION OF";S5;"KN/MM^2"

READY
RUN


EX3POINT2  3-JUN-81  14:05:56

ANALYSIS OF TENSION TESTS
-----------------------------

AREA         LENGTH       FORCE        EXTENSION    MODULUS E
(MM^2)       (MM)         (KN)         (MM)         (KN/MM^2)
  78           50          6.68         .021        203.907
  80           50          7.49         .023        203.533
  77           50          5.85         .019        199.932
  79           25          7.31         .011        210.299
  78           25          7.86         .012        209.936
AVERAGE VALUE OF E IS 205.521 KN/MM^2
WITH A STANDARD DEVIATION OF 4.47563 KN/MM^2

READY
```

Program notes

(1) The calculation of Young's modulus (E) in line 200 combines Equations (3.3), (3.2) and (3.1).

(2) The data is provided using DATA statements placed at the beginning of the program where they can be easily changed. The main program statements start at line 100 so that changes in data do not interfere with them. There are N sets of data, the number N being read from the first data statement.

(3) The average value of E is found by adding the values from individual tests (giving S1) and dividing by the number of tests (N). S1 is set to zero before the summation (line 150).

(4) The standard deviation is represented by S5. For a small sample

$$S5 = \sqrt{\left[\frac{N \sum_{i=1}^{N} E_i^2 - \left(\sum_{i=1}^{N} E_i \right)^2}{N(N-1)} \right]} \qquad (3.11)$$

where E_i is the value of modulus from an individual test. This equation is evaluated in line 260 with S2 as the sum of the squares of the individual E values.

Example 3.3 Design of tensile members using preferred sizes

Write a program to design tensile members of solid square or circular cross-section using the following preferred sizes (mm)

Example 3.3 Design of tensile members using preferred sizes   21

1, 1.2, 1.6, 2, 2.5, 3, 4, 5, 6, 8, 10, 12, 16, 20, 25, 30, 35, 40, 45, 50, 55, 60, 65, 70, 75, 80, 90, 100, 110, 120, 130, 140, 150, 160, 180, 190, 200, 220, 240, 260, 280, 300

The program should require 'run-time' input of maximum allowable tensile stress (N/mm^2) and tensile load (kN). The output should include the minimum cross-section area (mm^2) and preferred size dimensions for both square and circular sections. Because selection of a preferred size gives some overdesign, the output should also include the area of the selected preferred size, the actual working stress and the percentage overdesign (i.e. underutilisation of allowable stress).

Note: preferably, the preferred size selection should be written as a subroutine so that it can be readily used with other programs.

```
EX3POINT3   3-JUN-81   13:40:13

10 PRINT "DESIGN OF SQUARE AND CIRCULAR TENSILE MEMBERS USING PREFERRED SI
20 PRINT "----------------------------------------------------------------
30 PRINT
40 PRINT "INPUT:"
50 PRINT "MAX ALLOWABLE TENSILE STRESS (N/MM^2) - 0 TO STOP";
60 INPUT S1
70 IF S1>0 THEN 90
80 STOP
90 PRINT "MAX TENSILE LOAD (KN) ";
100 INPUT P1
110 P1=P1*1000
120 A1=P1/S1
130 PRINT
140 PRINT "MINIMUM CROSS-SECTION AREA ";A1;"MM^2"
150 PRINT
160 PRINT "SECTION "," ","ACTUAL AREA","ACTUAL STRESS","OVERDESIGN"
170 PRINT "(DIMENSION IN MM)","(MM^2)","(N/MM^2)","(PER CENT)"
180 D=SQR(A1)
190 GOSUB 1000
200 A=D*D
210 PRINT "SQUARE: SIDE LENGTH";D,A,P1/A,(A-A1)/A1*100
220 D=SQR(4*A1/3.14159)
230 GOSUB 1000
240 A=3.14159*D*D/4
250 PRINT "CIRCULAR: DIAMETER ";D,A,P1/A,(A-A1)/A*100
260 GO TO 30
1000 REM SELECTION OF PREFERRED SIZES - SQUARE OR CIRCULAR SECTIONS
1010 REM MODIFIES VALUE OF VARIABLE D TO A 'PREFERRED' SIZE
1020 REM USES VARIABLE NAMES I,N9,D9,D
1030 REM 'RESTORES' DATA BEFORE RETURNING TO MAIN PROGRAM
1040 DATA 43,1,1.2,1.6,2,2.5,3,4,5,6,8,10,12,16,20,25,30,35,40,45,50
1050 DATA 55,60,65,70,75,80,90,100,110,120,130,140,150,160,170,180
1060 DATA 190,200,220,240,260,280,300
1070 READ N9
1080 FOR I=1 TO N9
1090 READ D9
1100 IF D<=D9 THEN 1150
1110 NEXT I
1120 PRINT "DIMENSION D IS 300 OR LARGER"
1130 PRINT "THIS SUBROUTINE CANNOT PROVIDE A PREFERRED SIZE"
1140 GO TO 1160
1150 D=D9
1160 RESTORE
1170 RETURN

READY
```

```
RUN

EX3POINT3   3-JUN-81   13:41:17

DESIGN OF SQUARE AND CIRCULAR TENSILE MEMBERS USING PREFERRED SIZES
----------------------------------------------------------------------

INPUT:
MAX ALLOWABLE TENSILE STRESS (N/MM^2) - 0 TO STOP? 150
MAX TENSILE LOAD (KN) ? 115

MINIMUM CROSS-SECTION AREA   766.667 MM^2

SECTION                   ACTUAL AREA    ACTUAL STRESS OVERDESIGN
(DIMENSION IN MM)           (MM^2)        (N/MM^2)     (PER CENT)
SQUARE: SIDE LENGTH 30        900          127.778      17.3913
CIRCULAR: DIAMETER   35      962.112       119.529      20.3142

INPUT:
MAX ALLOWABLE TENSILE STRESS (N/MM^2) - 0 TO STOP? 50
MAX TENSILE LOAD (KN) ? 7000

MINIMUM CROSS-SECTION AREA   140000 MM^2

SECTION                   ACTUAL AREA    ACTUAL STRESS OVERDESIGN
(DIMENSION IN MM)           (MM^2)        (N/MM^2)     (PER CENT)
DIMENSION D IS 300 OR LARGER
THIS SUBROUTINE CANNOT PROVIDE A PREFERRED SIZE
SQUARE: SIDE LENGTH 374.166  140000         50             0
DIMENSION D IS 300 OR LARGER
THIS SUBROUTINE CANNOT PROVIDE A PREFERRED SIZE
CIRCULAR: DIAMETER  422.201  140000         50             0

INPUT:
MAX ALLOWABLE TENSILE STRESS (N/MM^2) - 0 TO STOP? 0

STOP AT LINE 80

READY
```

Program notes

(1) The input data is used to calculate the minimum required cross-section area A1 (line 120).

(2) From A1 the minimum side length D for a square section is determined (line 180) and the subroutine (lines 1000–1170) is used to modify D to the nearest (but higher) preferred size. The actual cross-section area A for this preferred size is then calculated (line 200) and the required output printed (line 210).

This procedure is repeated for a solid circular section (lines 220 to 250).

(3) The subroutine to select a preferred size starts with a number of descriptive REM statements so that it can be used in other programs with less chance of error (see Example 4.5).

There are N9 preferred sizes and as each is read by the subroutine (as D9 in line 1090) it is compared with the 'minimum' dimension D. More values are read until the first preferred size which exceeds D is found. The value of D is then changed to this preferred value (line 1150) and

Example 3.4 Impact loading   23

control is returned to the main program. If a large enough preferred size cannot be found a message is printed (lines 1120–1140) and the value of D is not modified.

Finally, the program restores the preferred size data so that it is again read from the beginning if another member is designed.

Example 3.4 Impact loading

Suppose a mass (weight W) falls under gravity through a height h before impacting a weightless collar at the end of a member length L and cross-section area A (Figure 3.3). It causes a sudden tensile load on the member that is higher than the static load due to the mass W.

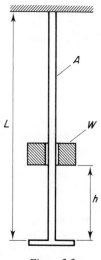

Figure 3.3

By equating the loss of potential energy of the weight to the gain in strain energy of the member as it extends to a maximum extension δ, show that the maximum tensile force P is given by

$$P = W\left[1 + \sqrt{\left(\frac{2hAE}{WL}\right)}\right] \tag{3.12}$$

if linear elastic stress–strain behaviour is assumed (Young's modulus E).

Write a program which, using 'run-time' input of mass (kg) and drop height (m), generates the maximum stresses and strains in the member (assuming linear elastic behaviour) for all combinations of the following

Young's modulus   :   2, 20 and 200 kN/mm^2
Member length   :   1, 10 and 100 m
Member diameter   :   5, 15 and 25 mm
(solid circular section)

Relate the results to the properties of some actual materials and note the influence of the various mass and member parameters.

```
EX3POINT4  3-JUN-81  13:45:07

10 PRINT "GRAVITIONAL IMPACT LOADING STRESSES AND STRAINS"
20 PRINT "----------------------------------------------------------------"
30 PRINT
40 PRINT "INPUT:"
50 PRINT "MASS OF FALLING WEIGHT (KG) - 0 TO STOP";
60 INPUT M
70 IF M>0 THEN 90
80 STOP
90 W=M*9.81
100 PRINT "DROP HEIGHT (M)";
110 INPUT H
120 H=H*1000
130 PRINT
140 PRINT "MODULUS E","LENGTH","DIAMETER","MAX STRESS","MAX STRAIN"
150 PRINT "(KN/MM^2)"," (M)"," (MM^2)"," (N/MM^2)","   (%)"
160 FOR E1=0 TO 2
170 E=2000*10^E1
180 FOR L1=0 TO 2
190 L=1000*10^L1
200 FOR D=5 TO 25 STEP 10
210 A=3.14159*D*D/4
220 P=W*(1+SQR(1+2*H*A*E/W/L))
230 PRINT E/1000,L/1000,D,P/A,100*P/A/E
240 NEXT D
250 PRINT
260 NEXT L1
270 PRINT
280 NEXT E1
290 GO TO 30

READY


RUN

EX3POINT4  3-JUN-81  13:45:46

GRAVITIONAL IMPACT LOADING STRESSES AND STRAINS
------------------------------------------------------------------

INPUT:
MASS OF FALLING WEIGHT (KG) - 0 TO STOP? 80
DROP HEIGHT (M)? 1
```

MODULUS E (KN/MM^2)	LENGTH (M)	DIAMETER (MM^2)	MAX STRESS (N/MM^2)	MAX STRAIN (%)
2	1	5	441.81	22.0905
2	1	15	137.798	6.88988
2	1	25	81.5843	4.07922
2	10	5	172.58	8.62898
2	10	15	46.8221	2.3411
2	10	25	26.9379	1.34689
2	100	5	96.5058	4.82529
2	100	15	18.4898	.924487
2	100	25	9.75399	.4877

Example 3.4 Impact loading   25

20	1	5	1305.03	6.52516
20	1	15	425.941	2.12971
20	1	25	254.49	1.27245
20	10	5	441.81	2.20905
20	10	15	137.798	.688988
20	10	25	81.5843	.407922
20	100	5	172.58	.862898
20	100	15	46.8221	.23411
20	100	25	26.9379	.134689
200	1	5	4038.65	2.01932
200	1	15	1337.27	.668637
200	1	25	801.296	.400648
200	10	5	1305.03	.652516
200	10	15	425.941	.212971
200	10	25	254.49	.127245
200	100	5	441.81	.220905
200	100	15	137.798	.0688988
200	100	25	81.5843	.0407922

```
INPUT:
MASS OF FALLING WEIGHT (KG) - 0 TO STOP? 0

STOP AT LINE 80

READY
```

Program notes

(1) The loss in potential energy of the falling weight is $W(h + \delta)$ which equals the gain in strain energy of the member (i.e. $\frac{1}{2} P \delta$ where P is the maximum force induced in the member).

From Equations (3.1), (3.2) and (3.3) assuming linear elastic behaviour

$$\delta = PL/AE \qquad (3.13)$$

hence

$$W(h + PL/AE) = P^2 L/2AE \qquad (3.14)$$

Solving this quadratic equation in P for the positive root gives the required expression for P. This is evaluated in line 220. Hence the maximum stress P/A is calculated and printed in line 230.

(2) The maximum strain $\delta/L = P/AE$ $\qquad (3.15)$

This is calculated and printed as a percentage in line 230.

(3) The calculations are performed using units of newtons and milli-metres. The input data is immediately converted to these units and is converted back to the original units if required for output (line 230).

(4) The range of values for E, L and diameter D are generated auto-matically by DO loops. Note the indirect way in which the values of E and L are determined (lines 170 and 190).

Example 3.5 Materials comparison

A range of materials with typical properties for short-term loading at 20°C is tabulated below.

Type	Material	Density (kg/m³)	Modulus E (kN/mm²)
Metal	Steel	7800	207
Metal	Aluminium (alloy)	2700	71
Metal	Brass	8800	117
Softwood	Spruce	480	9
Plastic	Polypropylene	900	1.4
Plastic	Acrylic	1180	3.1
Plastic	Polycarbonate	1200	2.4
Plastic	Rigid PVC	1390	3.4

Suppose these materials are made into members of equal length and with rectangular cross-sections of equal breadth but different thicknesses, in order to give them equal tensile stiffness.

Write a program to compare these materials in terms of their relative thickness and mass. The minor modifications to this program outlined in Problems (3.6) and (5.8) make the result much more interesting.

Hints:

(1) Read the data from DATA statements using subscripted variables. The program will then contain a statement such as

READ M$(I), R(I), E(I)

where I is the material number with a corresponding DATA statement for one of the materials

DATA "STEEL", 7800, 207

(2) Use material number 1 (e.g. steel) as a reference by setting its thickness to unity. Then calculate the thickness T(I) of each other material in order to give equal tensile stiffness.

The mass of the member using material number 1 should also be set to unity, the other materials having values of mass relative to this.

```
1 DATA 8
2 DATA "STEEL",7800,207
3 DATA "ALUMINIUM",2700,71
4 DATA "BRASS",8800,117
5 DATA "SPRUCE",480,9
```

Example 3.5 Materials comparison   27

```
6 DATA "POLYPROP.",,900,1.4
7 DATA "ACRYLIC",1180,3.1
8 DATA "POLYCARB.",1200,2.4
9 DATA "RIGID PVC",1390,3.4
100 PRINT "STRUCTURALLY EQUIVALENT MATERIALS COMPARISON"
110 PRINT "-----------------------------------------------"
120 PRINT
130 REM READ AND PRINT DATA
140 READ N
150 DIM M$(30),R(30),E(30),T(30),Z(30),A$(30),M(30)
160 PRINT "MATERIAL","DENSITY","MODULUS E"
170 PRINT " ","(KG/M^3)","(KN/MM^2)"
180 FOR I=1 TO N
190 READ M$(I),R(I),E(I)
200 PRINT M$(I),R(I),E(I)
210 NEXT I
220 REM DETERMINE RELATIVE THICKNESSES
230 PRINT
240 PRINT "EQUIVALENT TENSILE STIFFNESS COMPARISON"
250 T(1)=1
260 P$="THICKNESS"
270 FOR I=1 TO N
280 T(I)=T(1)*E(1)/E(I)
290 Z(I)=T(I)
300 A$(I)=M$(I)
310 NEXT I
320 REM RANK IN ORDER OF THICKNESS AND PRINT
330 GOSUB 1000
340 GOSUB 2000
350 REM DETERMINE RELATIVE MASSES
360 M(1)=1
370 P$="MASS"
380 FOR I=1 TO N
390 M(I)=M(1)*R(I)*T(I)/(R(1)*T(1))
400 Z(I)=M(I)
410 A$(I)=M$(I)
420 NEXT I
430 REM RANK IN ORDER OF MASS AND PRINT
440 GOSUB 1000
450 GOSUB 2000
460 STOP
1000 REM SUBROUTINE TO RANK N VALUES OF Z(I) IN DESCENDING ORDER
1010 REM WITH NAMES A$(I) SWAPPED TO MATCH Z(I)
1020 REM VARIABLE NAMES A9,B9,B$ ALSO USED
1030 A9=0
1040 FOR I=1 TO N-1
1050 IF Z(I)<=Z(I+1) THEN 1130
1060 A9=1
1070 B9=Z(I)
1080 Z(I)=Z(I+1)
1090 Z(I+1)=B9
1100 B$=A$(I)
1110 A$(I)=A$(I+1)
1120 A$(I+1)=B$
1130 NEXT I
1140 IF A9=1 THEN 1030
1150 RETURN
2000 REM SUBROUTINE TO PRINT COMPARISON OF MATERIALS
2010 REM IN ORDER OF PROPERTY P$
2020 PRINT
2030 PRINT "MATERIAL","RELATIVE ";P$
2040 FOR I=1 TO N
2050 PRINT I;A$(I),Z(I)
2060 NEXT I
2070 PRINT
2080 RETURN

READY

RUN
```

```
EX3POINTS   3-JUN-81   13:51:19

STRUCTURALLY EQUIVALENT MATERIALS COMPARISON
--------------------------------------------------

MATERIAL        DENSITY         MODULUS E
                (KG/M^3)        (KN/MM^2)
STEEL           7800            207
ALUMINIUM       2700            71
BRASS           8800            117
SPRUCE          480             9
POLYPROP.       900             1.4
ACRYLIC         1180            3.1
POLYCARB.       1200            2.4
RIGID PVC       1390            3.4

EQUIVALENT TENSILE STIFFNESS COMPARISON

MATERIAL        RELATIVE THICKNESS
  1 STEEL       1
  2 BRASS       1.76923
  3 ALUMINIUM   2.91549
  4 SPRUCE      23
  5 RIGID PVC   60.8824
  6 ACRYLIC     66.7742
  7 POLYCARB.   86.25
  8 POLYPROP.   147.857


MATERIAL        RELATIVE MASS
  1 STEEL       1
  2 ALUMINIUM   1.00921
  3 SPRUCE      1.41538
  4 BRASS       1.99606
  5 ACRYLIC     10.1017
  6 RIGID PVC   10.8495
  7 POLYCARB.   13.2692
  8 POLYPROP.   17.0604


STOP AT LINE 460

READY
```

Program notes

(1) Space for the subscripted variables has to be allocated using a DIM statement (line 150). In the above program, space has been given for up to 30 materials. On some computers a DIM statement of the form

    150 DIM M$(N), R(N), E(N)

is allowed enabling the exact space requirements to be set automatically.

(2) The values of thickness and mass are set for the first material (lines 250 and 360) and relative values are determined for the other materials (lines 280 and 390). A simple interchange of two DATA statements would allow a material other than steel to be used as the reference material.

(3) The subroutine in lines 1000 to 1150 is included because it is useful to print the comparisons in order of increasing thickness and mass. For this to be done without losing the association between each

material and its properties a copy A$(I) is made of each material name (lines 300 and 410). The subroutine ranks the materials in ascending order of the property Z(I). Each thickness is therefore copied to this name (line 290) as later is each mass (line 400).

To understand the ranking procedure (lines 1000 to 1150) it is beneficial to work through it with a simple example,

e.g using 4 values: $Z(1) = 5$, $Z(2) = 3$, $Z(3) = 4$ and $Z(4) = 2$.

The routine searches through the Z's, examines each value to see if it is less than the next (line 1050) and if it is not, the two Z's are swapped (lines 1070 to 1090) as are the corresponding material names (lines 1100 to 1130). The 'flag' A9 is used to check whether the ranking has been completed. At the start of each search it is set to zero (line 1030) and it is changed to 1 if a swap is necessary (line 1060). If no swap is necessary during a complete search through the Z's the value of A9 remains zero which signifies that the ranking has been completed.

(4) The use of subroutines to rank the results and then to print them is advantageous because these procedures are called for twice. A third call would be made if the program were to be extended to include material costs (Problem (3.6)).

The printing subroutine (lines 2000–2080) uses the variable P$ as part of a title. The appropriate value (THICKNESS or MASS) is set in the main program (lines 260 and 370).

PROBLEMS

(3.1) It is often necessary to make conversions from one set of units to another. For stress

$$1 \text{ N/mm}^2 = 10.197 \text{ kgf/cm}^2 = 145.04 \text{ lbf/in}^2$$

Write programs to convert between these units by

(1) printing values of stress in kgf/cm^2 and lbf/in^2 corresponding to 'run-time' input of stress in N/mm^2, and
(2) tabulating kgf/cm^2 and lbf/in^2 values corresponding to values of N/mm^2 from 0 to 200 N/mm^2 in steps of 10 N/mm^2.

This problem gives scope for a more ambitious programming task which is to write an 'interactive conversational' program to convert from any of the units to either or both of the others.

(3.2) Extend the program in Example 3.1 so that it determines Young's modulus (E in kN/mm^2) from additional 'run-time' input of length (L in mm) and extension of that length (x in mm).

Check that your program gives $E = 200 \text{ kN/mm}^2$ if $P = 8\text{kN}$, $A = 200 \text{ mm}^2$, $L = 50 \text{ mm}$ and $x = .01 \text{ mm}$.

(3.3) Modify the program in Example 3.1 so that the member cross-section can be specified by its diameter (if circular), its length and breadth (if square or rectangular) or directly by its area (if of any other shape).

(3.4) Write a program to design tensile members of solid rectangular cross-section chosen from all combinations of the following preferred sizes (mm)

> 10, 12, 16, 20, 25, 30, 35, 40, 45, 50, 55, 60, 65, 70, 75, 80, 90, 100

As in Example 3.3 the program requires input of maximum allowable tensile stress (N/mm^2) and tensile load (kN). The output should include the minimum cross-section area (mm^2) and dimensions for a range of preferred size rectangular selections. Because selection of a preferred size gives some overdesign, the output should also include the area of each preferred size section, its actual working stress and the percentage overdesign (i.e. underutilisation of allowable stress).

Hint: A possible scheme for the selection procedure is as follows.

(1) Read the N (= 18) preferred size data into a subscripted variable $D(I)$ where I varies from 1 to N. These represent one of the member dimensions.

(2) Set $I = 1$.

(3) RESTORE the data and then read them again, this time to represent the other member dimension B. As each value of B is read, the product $B \times D(I)$ equals a preferred size area. Compare this area with the minimum required area (A1 as in Example 3.3).

If $B \times D(I)$ is less than A1 the preferred size area is not large enough, so read the next data item as B.

If $B \times D(I)$ is greater than or equal to A1 a suitable preferred section has been found and its dimensions, actual working stress and percentage overdesign should be printed.

(4) Increase the value of I by 1 and repeat stage (3) to select another suitable preferred section. The program therefore tabulates up to N suitable sections. Not all of these are necessarily different (e.g. $20 \times 40 \equiv 40 \times 20$).

The section with the least overdesign can then be chosen manually.

The procedure outlined above could be modified in order to automatically select the section with the least overdesign. However, as availability is often an important consideration a restriction to one option is not necessarily advantageous.

(3.5) Consider a member subjected to gravitational tensile impact loading (see Example 3.4 and Figure 3.3). Write a program to determine the maximum mass which could be dropped on to the end of the member from a specified height and the maximum drop height for a specified mass.

The following data should be specified by run-time input

(1) the length and diameter of the member,
(2) Young's modulus for the member material and its maximum allowable tensile stress,
(3) a drop height from which the maximum mass (i.e. load capacity of the member) is to be determined,
(4) a value of mass, the maximum drop height of which is to be determined.

(3.6) Extend the materials comparison program of Example 3.5 to include a comparison of material costs for equivalent tensile stiffness.

The following are typical 1981 costs for the materials used in Example 3.5.

Material	Cost (pence/kg)
Steel	40
Aluminium	170
Brass	210
Spruce	50
Polypropylene	60
Acrylic	120
Polycarbonate	215
Rigid PVC	65

Note: cost data are inherently more variable and less reliable than physical or mechanical properties data.

Hint: If the material cost for a member made of material 1 is $P(1)$ then the cost for the equivalent member made of material I is given by

$$P(I) = \frac{P(1) \times M(I) \times C(I)}{M(1) \times C(1)}$$

where $M(I)$ is the mass of the member made of material I and $C(I)$ its cost per kilogram.

Other possible modifications to the program include

(1) swapping the data so that a material other than steel is the datum for comparison (i.e. material number 1),
(2) adding data for additional materials,
(3) comparing materials in terms of equivalent tensile strength.

(3.7) Modify the program in Example 3.3 in order to design a tensile member on a basis of maximum allowable deformation. To do this it is necessary to specify the member length, its maximum allowable extension and Young's modulus for the material to be used.

A further modification would allow a member to be designed using stress and deformation limits, the design being governed by whichever of the limits is reached first.

(3.8) Write a program to generate direct strains for a range of values of Poisson's ratio. Use the program to demonstrate that Poisson's ratio cannot exceed 0.5 for an isotropic material.

The program should require 'run-time' input of Young's modulus and direct stresses σ_x, σ_y and σ_z. For values of Poisson's ratio from, say, 0 to 0.8 in steps of 0.05 the program should use Equations (3.4) to tabulate values of ϵ_x, ϵ_y and ϵ_z (in microstrain) and the percentage volume increase for a unit cube.

Hints:
  (1) For a unit cube there is a volume increase from 1 to $(1 + \epsilon_x) \times (1 + \epsilon_y) \times (1 + \epsilon_z)$ when stressed.
  (2) When subjected to compressive hydrostatic stress ($\sigma_x = \sigma_y = \sigma_z < 0$) a body should decrease in volume.

(3.9) Solve Equations (3.8) and (3.10) to determine expressions for the direct stresses in the compound bar shown in Figure 3.2 when it is subjected to an axial load and a change in temperature.

Write a program to print these stresses for any material combination and for any axial and (or) thermal loading.

(3.10) Write a program (similar to that in Example 4.6) to fit a straight line to experimental load-extension data. Hence determine Young's modulus (E). It is necessary to specify the following data

  (1) the specimen diameter (mm),
  (2) the gauge length (mm) over which the extensions are measured,
  (3) the number of data pairs, i.e. the number of load levels,
  (4) each data pair, i.e. load (kN) and extension (mm).

In addition to Young's modulus the program should output the straight line parameters m (gradient) and c (intercept) and a table of the experimental values of load and extension, the corresponding predicted values of extension and their errors.

Chapter 4

Shear and torsion

ESSENTIAL THEORY

4.1 Shear stress

Shear stress is the stress component parallel to the plane on which it acts. With the notation shown in Figure 4.1 the shear stress is defined as

$$\tau = Q/A \qquad (4.1)$$

where τ represents the actual (uniform) stress if the force Q is uniformly distributed over the area A and the average stress if Q is not uniformly distributed. In the latter case the actual shear stress at any point can be defined by the limiting ratio of $\delta Q/\delta A$ where δA represents the area of a small element of material over which the stress can reasonably be assumed to be uniform.

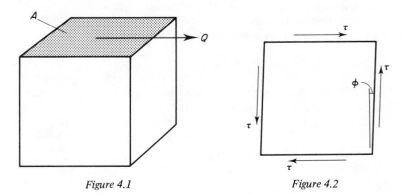

| *Figure 4.1* | *Figure 4.2* |

In order to preserve equilibrium every shear stress (τ) is accompanied by an equal complementary shear stress on a plane at right angles as shown in Figure 4.2.

33

4.2 Shear strain

Shear strain (γ) is a dimensionless measure of the distortion of a rectangular element under shear. For small strains

$$\gamma = \tan\phi \simeq \phi \tag{4.2}$$

where ϕ is the angle shown in Figure 4.2 measured in radians.

4.3 Stress-strain relations

The shear stress—shear strain relationships are qualitatively similar to the direct stress—direct strain relationships described in Section 3.2. In the linear elastic region where Hooke's Law is obeyed, the gradient of the shear stress—strain curve is a constant called *shear modulus* (G, modulus of rigidity) where

$$G = \tau/\gamma \tag{4.3}$$

4.4 Relationship between elastic constants

When the material behaviour is linearly elastic and isotropic (properties independent of direction) there are only two independent elastic constants.

The shear modulus (G) is related to Young's modulus (E) and Poisson's ratio (ν) by the equation

$$E = 2G(1 + \nu) \tag{4.4}$$

If any two of the constants are known the third can be found from this equation.

A fourth, less commonly used, elastic constant is bulk modulus. This represents a volumetric stress divided by volumetric strain. Thus

$$K = \frac{P}{(\delta V/V)} \tag{4.5}$$

where P is a compressive hydrostatic stress (equal in all directions) and δV is the decrease in an initial volume V.

Bulk modulus is related to the other elastic constants by the equation

$$E = 3K(1 - \nu) \tag{4.6}$$

4.5 Torsion of circular shafts

Consider the solid circular shaft shown in Figure 4.3 which is held at the left-hand end and subjected to a torque T about the longitudinal axis at the right-hand end.

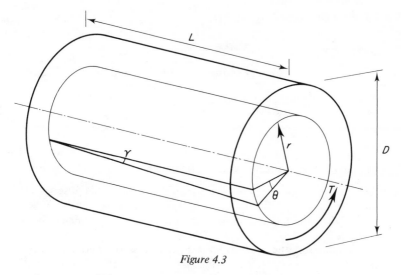

Figure 4.3

It is assumed that

(1) twisting is uniform along the shaft,
(2) cross-sections remain plane and radii straight,
(3) neither the length L or diameter D change,
(4) the material of the shaft is homogeneous, isotropic and obeys Hooke's law.

The analysis requires consideration of equilibrium, compatibility and the stress–strain relationship, i.e. all the 'tools' of stress analysis.

Compatibility relates the shear strain at a radius r to the angle of twist θ over the length L of the shaft. Equilibrium of an elemental tube radius r relates the shear stress τ at that radius to the torque T and the polar second moment of area J. When the stress-strain relation, Equation (4.3), is included the following equation can be derived

$$\tau/r = T/J = G\theta/L \qquad (4.7)$$

The shear stress τ varies linearly with r being zero at the centre of the shaft and a maximum at the outside.

The polar second moment of area J is given by the equation

$$J = \int_0^{D/2} r^2 \, dA \qquad (4.8)$$

where dA is the cross-section area of the elemental tube radius r ($dA = 2\pi r \, dr$).

For a solid shaft of diameter D

$$J = \pi D^4 / 32 \qquad (4.9)$$

For a hollow shaft of external diameter D_2 and internal diameter D_1

$$J = \frac{\pi(D_2{}^4 - D_1{}^4)}{32} \qquad (4.10)$$

WORKED EXAMPLES

Example 4.1 Pressure vessel safety valve design

A simple safety valve for a pressure vessel is a small circular disc set into a hole in the wall of the vessel which fails in shear around its circumference when the internal pressure reaches some predetermined 'blow-out' value.

By considering the equilibrium of such a disc valve, derive a relationship between the diameter and thickness of the disc, its shear strength and the required blow-out pressure.

Write a program which, for 'run-time' input of shear strength and blow-out pressure, determines the necessary disc thickness for the range of disc diameters: 25, 50, 75, 100, 125 and 150 mm.

Extend the program so that the required thickness can be found for any specified thickness and vice-versa.

```
EX4POINT1 15-JUN-81  10:21:32

10 PRINT "SELECTION OF PRESSURE VESSEL SAFETY VALVES"
20 PRINT "----------------------------------------------"
30 PRINT
40 PRINT "INPUT:"
50 PRINT "SHEAR STRENGTH OF VALVE MATERIAL (N/MM^2)";
60 INPUT S
70 PRINT "REQUIRED BLOW-OUT PRESSURE (N/MM^2)";
80 INPUT P
90 PRINT
100 PRINT "POSSIBLE DISC VALVE DIMENSIONS:"
110 PRINT "DIAMETER (MM)","THICKNESS (MM)"
120 FOR D=25 TO 150 STEP 25
130 T=P*D/4/S
140 PRINT D,T
150 NEXT D
160 PRINT
170 PRINT "INPUT 0(TO STOP),+VE VALUE(TO SPECIFY DIAMETER),"
180 PRINT "-VE VALUE(TO SPECIFY THICKNESS)";
190 INPUT Z
200 IF Z<>0 THEN 220
210 STOP
220 IF Z<0 THEN 260
230 D=Z
240 PRINT "REQUIRED THICKNESS";P*D/4/S;"MM"
250 GO TO 160
260 T=-Z
270 PRINT "REQUIRED DIAMETER";4*S*T/P;"MM"
280 GO TO 160

READY
```

Example 4.2 Simple riveted joint analysis 37

```
RUN

EX4POINT1  7-MAY-82  09:48:16

SELECTION OF PRESSURE VESSEL SAFETY VALVES
----------------------------------------------

INPUT:
SHEAR STRENGTH OF VALVE MATERIAL (N/MM^2)? 150
REQUIRED BLOW-OUT PRESSURE (N/MM^2)? 5

POSSIBLE DISC VALVE DIMENSIONS:
DIAMETER (MM) THICKNESS (MM)
  25          .208333
  50          .416667
  75          .625
 100          .833333
 125         1.04167
 150         1.25

INPUT 0(TO STOP),+VE VALUE(TO SPECIFY DIAMETER),
-VE VALUE(TO SPECIFY THICKNESS)? -.5
REQUIRED DIAMETER 60 MM

INPUT 0(TO STOP),+VE VALUE(TO SPECIFY DIAMETER),
-VE VALUE(TO SPECIFY THICKNESS)? 80
REQUIRED THICKNESS .666667 MM

INPUT 0(TO STOP),+VE VALUE(TO SPECIFY DIAMETER),
-VE VALUE(TO SPECIFY THICKNESS)? 0

STOP AT LINE 210

READY
```

Program notes

(1) Suppose the disc has a diameter d, thickness t and shear strength s. If the blow-out pressure is P an equlibrium equation gives

$$P.\pi d^2/4 = s.\pi dt \qquad (4.11)$$

hence $\qquad t = pd/4s$

(2) The program extension which enables individual values of diameter or thickness to be specified starts in line 170. This allows either the thickness *or* the diameter to be input (as Z) in line 190. If Z is positive the program interprets it as a diameter (line 230) and the corresponding thickness is calculated. If Z is negative it is interpreted as specifying the disc thickness and the negative Z is changed to a positive thickness in line 260.

Example 4.2 Simple riveted joint analysis

A simple riveted (or bolted) connection is shown in Figure 4.4. The stress distribution around such a connection is complex but usual design procedures assume the stresses are uniformly distributed. (The behaviour of riveted and bolted connections is discussed more fully in the references on page 13.)

The joint can fail by

(1) shearing the rivets between the plates,
(2) crushing between the rivet and a plate,
(3) tearing a plate across section XX,

or, if there is not sufficient overlap between the two plates by

(4) shear of a plate along the dotted lines in Figure 4.4.

For a joint of given dimensions the load capacity is governed by the most critical of the above failure modes. The load capacity is therefore the least of

(a) $\tau_r \dfrac{\pi d^2}{4}$ where τ_r is the maximum allowable shear stress in the rivet,

(b) $\sigma_b dt$ where σ_b is the maximum allowable bearing (crushing) stress between rivet and plate,

(c) $\sigma_p (b - d)t$ where σ_p is the maximum allowable tensile stress in the plate material,

(d) $\tau_p 2ht$ where τ_p is the maximum allowable shear stress in the plate material

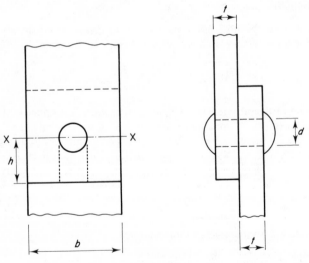

Figure 4.4

Example 4.2 Simple riveted joint analysis 39

The percentage efficiency of the joint is given by

$$\frac{\text{least load capacity}}{\text{load capacity of plate}} \times 100$$

where the load capacity of the plate equals $\sigma_p bt$

Write a program to determine the load capacity and efficiency of the simple riveted joint shown in Figure 4.4 for the first three failure modes outlined above. The program should enable the rivet diameter to be varied so that its optimum size for maximum joint efficiency can be determined.

Typical allowable stress values are

$$\tau_r = 75 \text{ N/mm}^2, \sigma_b = 180 \text{ N/mm}^2, \sigma_p = 150 \text{ N/mm}^2$$

```
EX4POINT2 15-JUN-81  10:29:50

10 PRINT "LOAD CAPACITY AND OPTIMUM RIVET SIZE FOR SIMPLE JOINT"
20 PRINT "------------------------------------------------------------"
30 PRINT
40 PRINT "INPUT:"
50 PRINT "MAX ALLOWABLE SHEAR STRESS IN RIVET (N/MM^2)";
60 INPUT R1
70 PRINT "MAX ALLOWABLE TENSILE STRESS IN PLATE (N/MM^2)";
80 INPUT P1
90 PRINT "MAX ALLOWABLE BEARING PRESSURE ON PLATE (N/MM^2)";
100 INPUT B1
110 PRINT
120 PRINT "PLATE WIDTH (MM)";
130 INPUT B
140 PRINT "PLATE THICKNESS (MM)";
150 INPUT T
160 F1=P1*B*T
170 PRINT
180 PRINT "RIVET DIAMETER (MM) - 0 TO STOP, -VE TO CHANGE PLATE DIMENSIONS";
190 INPUT D
200 IF D<0 THEN 110
210 IF D>0 THEN 230
220 STOP
230 PRINT "LOAD CAPACITIES:"
240 R2=R1*3.14149*D*D/4
250 PRINT "RIVET SHEAR:";R2/1000;"KN","EFFICIENCY";100*R2/F1;"%"
260 B2=B1*D*T
270 PRINT "PLATE CRUSH:";B2/1000;"KN","EFFICIENCY";100*B2/F1;"%"
280 P2=P1*(B-D)*T
290 PRINT "PLATE TEAR:";P2/1000;"KN","EFFICIENCY";100*P2/F1;"%"
300 GO TO 170

READY


RUN


EX4POINT2 15-JUN-81   10:30:59

LOAD CAPACITY AND OPTIMUM RIVET SIZE FOR SIMPLE JOINT
------------------------------------------------------------

INPUT:
MAX ALLOWABLE SHEAR STRESS IN RIVET (N/MM^2)? 75
MAX ALLOWABLE TENSILE STRESS IN PLATE (N/MM^2)? 150
MAX ALLOWABLE BEARING PRESSURE ON PLATE (N/MM^2)? 180
```

```
PLATE WIDTH (MM)? 50
PLATE THICKNESS (MM)? 5

RIVET DIAMETER (MM) - 0 TO STOP, -VE TO CHANGE PLATE DIMENSIONS? 20
LOAD CAPACITIES:
RIVET SHEAR: 23.5612 KN      EFFICIENCY 62.8298 %
PLATE CRUSH: 18 KN           EFFICIENCY 48 %
PLATE TEAR: 22.5 KN          EFFICIENCY 60 %

RIVET DIAMETER (MM) - 0 TO STOP, -VE TO CHANGE PLATE DIMENSIONS? 25
LOAD CAPACITIES:
RIVET SHEAR: 36.8143 KN      EFFICIENCY 98.1716 %
PLATE CRUSH: 22.5 KN         EFFICIENCY 60 %
PLATE TEAR: 18.75 KN         EFFICIENCY 50 %

RIVET DIAMETER (MM) - 0 TO STOP, -VE TO CHANGE PLATE DIMENSIONS? 22.5
LOAD CAPACITIES:
RIVET SHEAR: 29.8196 KN      EFFICIENCY 79.519 %
PLATE CRUSH: 20.25 KN        EFFICIENCY 54 %
PLATE TEAR: 20.625 KN        EFFICIENCY 55 %

RIVET DIAMETER (MM) - 0 TO STOP, -VE TO CHANGE PLATE DIMENSIONS? -1

PLATE WIDTH (MM)? 60
PLATE THICKNESS (MM)? 5

RIVET DIAMETER (MM) - 0 TO STOP, -VE TO CHANGE PLATE DIMENSIONS? 22.5
LOAD CAPACITIES:
RIVET SHEAR: 29.8196 KN      EFFICIENCY 66.2658 %
PLATE CRUSH: 20.25 KN        EFFICIENCY 45 %
PLATE TEAR: 28.125 KN        EFFICIENCY 62.5 %

RIVET DIAMETER (MM) - 0 TO STOP, -VE TO CHANGE PLATE DIMENSIONS? 25
LOAD CAPACITIES:
RIVET SHEAR: 36.8143 KN      EFFICIENCY 81.8096 %
PLATE CRUSH: 22.5 KN         EFFICIENCY 50 %
PLATE TEAR: 26.25 KN         EFFICIENCY 58.3333 %

RIVET DIAMETER (MM) - 0 TO STOP, -VE TO CHANGE PLATE DIMENSIONS? 0

STOP AT LINE 220

READY
```

Program notes

(1) The load capacity of the plate (F1) is calculated in line 160.
(2) The input for rivet diameter enables the program to stop or the plate dimensions to be changed (lines 190 to 210).

Example 4.3 Relation between elastic constants

For an isotropic, linearly elastic material the elastic constants Young's modulus (E), shear modulus (G) and Poisson's ratio (v) are related by the equation

$$E = 2G(1 + v)$$

By differentiating this equation it is possible to relate the maximum errors in determining the constants. Thus

$$dE = 2(1 + v)dG + 2Gdv$$

Example 4.3 Relation between elastic constants   41

from which

$$\frac{dE}{E} = \frac{2(1 + \nu)}{E} dG + \frac{2G}{E} d\nu$$

and

$$\frac{dE}{E} = \frac{2(1 + \nu)}{E} G \frac{dG}{G} + \frac{2G\nu}{E} \frac{d\nu}{\nu}$$

or

$$\frac{dE}{E} = \frac{dG}{G} + \frac{\nu}{1 + \nu} \frac{d\nu}{\nu} \qquad (4.12)$$

Hence if E is derived from G and ν then the maximum error in E (namely dE/E) can be determined from the maximum errors in the other constants (dG/G and $d\nu/\nu$).

Write a program to determine the third constant and its maximum error from values of the other two constants and their maximum errors.

```
EX4POINT3 15-JUN-81  10:40:20

10 PRINT "ELASTIC CONSTANT CONVERSION AND ERROR ANALYSIS"
20 PRINT "----------------------------------------------------"
30 PRINT
40 PRINT "YOUNG'S MODULUS (E), SHEAR MODULUS (G) AND POISSON'S RATIO (U)"
50 PRINT "ARE RELATED FOR AN ISOTROPIC LINEARLY ELASTIC MATERIAL."
60 PRINT "THIS PROGRAM FINDS THE THIRD CONSTANT AND ITS MAXIMUM ERROR"
70 PRINT "FROM VALUES OF THE OTHER TWO CONSTANTS AND THEIR MAXIMUM ERRORS"
80 PRINT
90 PRINT "NOTE: INPUT ZERO FOR THE UNKNOWN CONSTANT"
100 PRINT
110 PRINT "INPUT YOUNG'S MODULUS E (KN/MM^2) ";
120 INPUT E
130 IF E=0 THEN 160
140 PRINT "       MAXIMUM ERROR IN E (%) ";
150 INPUT E1
160 PRINT "INPUT SHEAR MODULUS G (KN/MM^2) ";
170 INPUT G
180 IF G=0 THEN 210
190 PRINT "       MAXIMUM ERROR IN G (%) ";
200 INPUT G1
210 PRINT "INPUT POISSON'S RATIO U ";
220 INPUT U
230 IF U=0 THEN 260
240 PRINT "       MAXIMUM ERROR IN U (%) ";
250 INPUT U1
260 PRINT
270 IF E=0 THEN 320
280 IF G=0 THEN 360
290 IF U=0 THEN 400
300 PRINT "YOU HAVE SPECIFIED ALL THREE CONSTANTS!"
310 GO TO 80
320 E=2*G*(1+U)
330 E1=U1*U/(1+U)+G1
340 PRINT "YOUNG'S MODULUS";E;"KN/MM^2   MAXIMUM ERROR";E1;"%"
350 GO TO 80
360 G=E/2/(1+U)
370 G1=E1+U1*U/(1+U)
```

```
380 PRINT "SHEAR MODULUS";G;"KN/MM^2    MAXIMUM ERROR";G1;"%"
390 GO TO 80
400 U=E/2/G-1
410 U1=E/(E-2*G)*(E1+G1)
420 PRINT "POISSON'S RATIO";U;"    MAXIMUM ERROR";U1;"%"
430 GO TO 80
```

READY

RUN

EX4POINT3 15-JUN-81   10:41:18

ELASTIC CONSTANT CONVERSION AND ERROR ANALYSIS

YOUNG'S MODULUS (E), SHEAR MODULUS (G) AND POISSON'S RATIO (U)
ARE RELATED FOR AN ISOTROPIC LINEARLY ELASTIC MATERIAL.
THIS PROGRAM FINDS THE THIRD CONSTANT AND ITS MAXIMUM ERROR
FROM VALUES OF THE OTHER TWO CONSTANTS AND THEIR MAXIMUM ERRORS

NOTE: INPUT ZERO FOR THE UNKNOWN CONSTANT

INPUT YOUNG'S MODULUS E (KN/MM^2) ? 205
      MAXIMUM ERROR IN E (%) ? 5
INPUT SHEAR MODULUS G (KN/MM^2) ? 0
INPUT POISSON'S RATIO U ? .3
      MAXIMUM ERROR IN U (%) ? 10

SHEAR MODULUS 78.8462 KN/MM^2   MAXIMUM ERROR 7.30769 %

NOTE: INPUT ZERO FOR THE UNKNOWN CONSTANT

INPUT YOUNG'S MODULUS E (KN/MM^2) ? 205
      MAXIMUM ERROR IN E (%) ? 1
INPUT SHEAR MODULUS G (KN/MM^2) ? 80
      MAXIMUM ERROR IN G (%) ? 1
INPUT POISSON'S RATIO U ? 0

POISSON'S RATIO .28125   MAXIMUM ERROR 9.11111 %

NOTE: INPUT ZERO FOR THE UNKNOWN CONSTANT

INPUT YOUNG'S MODULUS E (KN/MM^2) ? 0
INPUT SHEAR MODULUS G (KN/MM^2) ? 80
      MAXIMUM ERROR IN G (%) ? 2
INPUT POISSON'S RATIO U ? .3
      MAXIMUM ERROR IN U (%) ? 5

YOUNG'S MODULUS 208 KN/MM^2   MAXIMUM ERROR 3.15385 %

NOTE: INPUT ZERO FOR THE UNKNOWN CONSTANT

INPUT YOUNG'S MODULUS E (KN/MM^2) ?

STOP AT LINE 120

READY
```

### Program notes

(1) The program interprets a zero input value of any of the constants as indicating that the constant is unknown (lines 130, 180 and 230).

(2) Line 300 is reached if all three constants are specified. A warning message is then printed and the data have to be input again (correctly!).
```

Example 4.4 Design of circular shaft   43

There is, however, a flaw in the program as written above. It is possible to input zero for two of the constants thereby classifying them as unknown and causing an erroneous prediction of the third constant. It is a useful exercise to modify the program so that it is necessary to specify non-zero values for two of the constants.

(3) If E and ν are specified, the maximum error in G (G1 in line 370) is given by the equation

$$\frac{\mathrm{d}G}{G} = \frac{\mathrm{d}E}{E} + \frac{\nu}{1+\nu} \frac{\mathrm{d}\nu}{\nu} \qquad (4.13)$$

and if E and G are specified the error in ν (U1 in line 410) is given by the equation

$$\frac{\mathrm{d}\nu}{\nu} = \frac{E}{(E-2G)} \left(\frac{\mathrm{d}E}{E} + \frac{\mathrm{d}G}{G} \right) \qquad (4.14)$$

For all cases in the above program the errors are expressed as percentages.

Example 4.4 Design of circular shafts

Write a program to design (i.e. determine the diameter of) a solid circular shaft to resist a prescribed torque. In addition to specifying the applied torque (in kNm) there should be 'run-time' input of the maximum allowable shear stress (N/mm^2) and maximum allowable angle of twist per metre length (o/m). The material shear modulus (G in kN/mm^2) must also be specified.

The program should determine whether the design is stress or deflection (twist) limited and then determine the required shaft diameter. The program should also print the 'non-limiting' value of maximum shear stress or twist per metre length in the designed shaft.

```
EX4POINT4 15-JUN-81  11:26:58

10 PRINT "DESIGN OF SOLID CIRCULAR SHAFTS"
20 PRINT "---------------------------------------"
30 PRINT
40 PRINT "INPUT:"
50 PRINT "APPLIED TORQUE (KNM) - 0 TO STOP";
60 INPUT T
70 IF T>0 THEN 90
80 STOP
90 T=T*1.00000E+06
100 PRINT "MAX ALLOWABLE SHEAR STRESS (N/MM^2)";
110 INPUT S
120 PRINT "MAX ALLOWABLE TWIST PER METRE LENGTH (DEG/M)";
130 INPUT A
140 A=A*3.14159/180/1000
150 PRINT "SHEAR MODULUS G (KN/MM^2)";
160 INPUT G
170 G=G*1000
```

```
180 PRINT
190 REM DIAMETER D1 FOR MAX STRESS NOT TO BE EXCEEDED
200 D1=(16*T/3.14159/S)^(1/3)
210 REM DIAMETER D2 FOR MAX TWIST NOT TO BE EXCEEDED
220 D2=(32*T/(G*A*3.14159))^(1/4)
230 IF D1>D2 THEN 290
240 S=16*T/3.14159/D2^3
250 PRINT "DEFLECTION (TWIST) LIMITED DESIGN:"
260 PRINT "MAXIMUM STRESS";S;"N/MM^2"
270 PRINT "REQUIRED SHAFT DIAMETER";D2;"MM"
280 GO TO 30
290 A=32*T/(G*D1^4*3.14159)
300 PRINT "STRESS LIMITED DESIGN:"
310 PRINT "MAXIMUM TWIST PER METRE LENGTH";A*1000*180/3.14159;"DEG"
320 PRINT "REQUIRED SHAFT DIAMETER";D1;"MM"
330 GO TO 30

READY

RUN

EX4POINT4  15-JUN-81   11:27:45

DESIGN OF SOLID CIRCULAR SHAFTS
----------------------------------------------

INPUT:
APPLIED TORQUE (KNM) - 0 TO STOP? 40
MAX ALLOWABLE SHEAR STRESS (N/MM^2)? 55
MAX ALLOWABLE TWIST PER METRE LENGTH (DEG/M)? 1
SHEAR MODULUS G (KN/MM^2)? 80

STRESS LIMITED DESIGN:
MAXIMUM TWIST PER METRE LENGTH .509177 DEG
REQUIRED SHAFT DIAMETER 154.723 MM

INPUT:
APPLIED TORQUE (KNM) - 0 TO STOP? 40
MAX ALLOWABLE SHEAR STRESS (N/MM^2)? 55
MAX ALLOWABLE TWIST PER METRE LENGTH (DEG/M)? .5
SHEAR MODULUS G (KN/MM^2)? 80

DEFLECTION (TWIST) LIMITED DESIGN:
MAXIMUM STRESS 54.2547 N/MM^2
REQUIRED SHAFT DIAMETER 155.429 MM

INPUT:
APPLIED TORQUE (KNM) - 0 TO STOP? 40
MAX ALLOWABLE SHEAR STRESS (N/MM^2)? 55
MAX ALLOWABLE TWIST PER METRE LENGTH (DEG/M)? .2
SHEAR MODULUS G (KN/MM^2)? 80

DEFLECTION (TWIST) LIMITED DESIGN:
MAXIMUM STRESS 27.2887 N/MM^2
REQUIRED SHAFT DIAMETER 195.441 MM

INPUT:
APPLIED TORQUE (KNM) - 0 TO STOP? 0

STOP AT LINE 80

READY
```

Program notes

(1) The data are input in their most convenient units. They are immediately converted to units of newtons, millimetres and radians (lines 90, 140, 170). The calculations are then done in these basic consistent units.

Example 4.5 Design of circular shaft using preferred sizes   45

(2) The design procedure uses Equations (4.7) and (4.9).

If the design is determined by the maximum allowable shear stress which the shaft material can sustain then

$$\tau_{max}/r_{max} = T/J = 32T/\pi D^4 \qquad (4.15)$$

where τ_{max} is the maximum allowable shear stress (S) and r_{max} is $D/2$ because the maximum stress occurs at the outside of the shaft.

If the design is determined by the angle of twist (per metre length) which the shaft is allowed to sustain then

$$G\theta/L = T/J = 32T/\pi D^4 \qquad (4.16)$$

where θ is the maximum allowable angle of twist (in radians) over a length L.

(3) The program first determines the required diameter assuming the design is stress limited (D1 in line 200). It then determines the required diameter assuming the design is limited by the maximum allowable twist (D2 in line 220). The design is determined by the less of these values (line 230).

(4) If the design is deflection (twist) limited the required diameter is D2. The maximum shear stress in a shaft of that diameter is then determined (line 240). A similar, but reversed, procedure is used if the design is stress limited (lines 290 to 330).

Example 4.5 Design of circular shaft using preferred sizes

Write a program to design a solid circular shaft to resist a prescribed torque using the preferred sizes for shaft diameter detailed in Example 3.3.

The required data specification is outlined in Example 4.4. The program should output the actual values of maximum shear stress and twist per metre length whether the design is stress or deflection (twist) limited.

```
EX4POINT5 15-JUN-81  10:16:41

10 PRINT "DESIGN OF SOLID CIRCULAR SHAFTS USING PREFERRED SIZES"
20 PRINT "------------------------------------------------------------"
30 PRINT
40 PRINT "INPUT:"
50 PRINT "APPLIED TORQUE (KNM) - 0 TO STOP";
60 INPUT T
70 IF T>0 THEN 90
80 STOP
90 T=T*1.00000E+06
100 PRINT "MAXIMUM ALLOWABLE SHEAR STRESS (N/MM^2)";
110 INPUT S
120 PRINT "MAXIMUM ALLOWABLE TWIST PER METRE LENGTH (DEG/M)";
130 INPUT A
140 A=A*3.14159/180/1000
150 PRINT "SHEAR MODULUS G (KN/MM^2)";
```

```
160 INPUT G
170 G=G*1000
180 PRINT
190 REM DIAMETER D1 FOR MAX STRESS NOT TO BE EXCEEDED
200 D1=(16*T/3.14159/S)^(1/3)
210 D=D1
220 GOSUB 1000
230 D1=D
240 REM DIAMETER D2 FOR MAX TWIST NOT TO BE EXCEEDED
250 D2=(32*T/(G*A*3.14159))^(1/4)
260 D=D2
270 GOSUB 1000
280 D2=D
290 IF D1>D2 THEN 330
300 D=D2
310 PRINT "DEFLECTION (TWIST) LIMITED DESIGN:"
320 GO TO 350
330 D=D1
340 PRINT "STRESS LIMITED DESIGN:"
350 A=32*T/(G*D^4*3.14159)
360 S=16*T/3.14159/D^3
370 PRINT "MAXIMUM TWIST PER METRE LENGTH";A*1000*180/3.14159;"DEG"
380 PRINT "MAXIMUM STRESS";S;"N/MM^2"
390 PRINT "REQUIRED SHAFT DIAMETER (PREFERRED SIZE)";D;"MM"
400 GO TO 30
1000 REM SELECTION OF PREFERRED SIZES - SQUARE OR CIRCULAR SECTIONS
1010 REM MODIFIES VALUE OF VARIABLE D TO A 'PREFERRED' SIZE
1020 REM USES VARIABLE NAMES I,N9,D9,D
1030 REM 'RESTORES' DATA BEFORE RETURNING TO MAIN PROGRAM
1040 DATA 43,1,1.2,1.6,2,2.5,3,4,5,6,8,10,12,16,20,25,30,35,40,45,50
1050 DATA 55,60,65,70,75,80,90,100,110,120,130,140,150,160,170,180
1060 DATA 190,200,220,240,260,280,300
1070 READ N9
1080 FOR I=1 TO N9
1090 READ D9
1100 IF D<=D9 THEN 1150
1110 NEXT I
1120 PRINT "DIMENSION D IS 300 OR LARGER"
1130 PRINT "THIS SUBROUTINE CANNOT PROVIDE A PREFERRED SIZE"
1140 GO TO 1160
1150 D=D9
1160 RESTORE
1170 RETURN

READY


RUN


EX4POINT5 15-JUN-81  10:17:55

DESIGN OF SOLID CIRCULAR SHAFTS USING PREFERRED SIZES
------------------------------------------------------

INPUT:
APPLIED TORQUE (KNM) - 0 TO STOP? 40
MAXIMUM ALLOWABLE SHEAR STRESS (N/MM^2)? 55
MAXIMUM ALLOWABLE TWIST PER METRE LENGTH (DEG/M)? 1
SHEAR MODULUS G (KN/MM^2)? 80

STRESS LIMITED DESIGN:
MAXIMUM TWIST PER METRE LENGTH .44526 DEG
MAXIMUM STRESS 49.736 N/MM^2
REQUIRED SHAFT DIAMETER (PREFERRED SIZE) 160 MM

INPUT:
APPLIED TORQUE (KNM) - 0 TO STOP? 40
MAXIMUM ALLOWABLE SHEAR STRESS (N/MM^2)? 55
MAXIMUM ALLOWABLE TWIST PER METRE LENGTH (DEG/M)? .5
SHEAR MODULUS G (KN/MM^2)? 80
```

Example 4.6 Least squares analysis of torque-twist data   47

```
DEFLECTION (TWIST) LIMITED DESIGN:
MAXIMUM TWIST PER METRE LENGTH .44526 DEG
MAXIMUM STRESS 49.736 N/MM^2
REQUIRED SHAFT DIAMETER (PREFERRED SIZE) 160 MM

INPUT:
APPLIED TORQUE (KNM) - 0 TO STOP? 40
MAXIMUM ALLOWABLE SHEAR STRESS (N/MM^2)? 55
MAXIMUM ALLOWABLE TWIST PER METRE LENGTH (DEG/M)? .2
SHEAR MODULUS G (KN/MM^2)? 80

DEFLECTION (TWIST) LIMITED DESIGN:
MAXIMUM TWIST PER METRE LENGTH .182378 DEG
MAXIMUM STRESS 25.4648 N/MM^2
REQUIRED SHAFT DIAMETER (PREFERRED SIZE) 200 MM

INPUT:
APPLIED TORQUE (KNM) - 0 TO STOP? 0

STOP AT LINE 80

READY
```

Program notes

(1) Example 4.4, Program notes (1), (2) and (3) are relevant to this program also, though some of the line numbers are different.

(2) The subroutine to select the preferred size for shaft diameter is that used in Example 3.3 and described in Program note (3) for that program. This subroutine alters the value of dimension D to a preferred size. The calculated shaft diameters D1 and D2 are therefore converted to D before the subroutine is called and converted back to D1 and D2 afterwards (lines 210 to 230 and 260 to 280).

(3) Because the preferred diameter is higher than that directly required, neither the maximum shear stress nor the twist per metre length are the limiting values specified by the input data. After the program has determined whether the design is stress or twist limited (line 290), it sets the preferred size diameter to D (line 300 or 330) and then calculates the actual values of twist per metre length (line 350) and maximum shear stress (line 360).

Example 4.6 Least squares analysis of torque-twist data

To fit the best straight line through a set of experimental data the principle of least squares can be used. This states that the best fit is that for which the sum of the squares of the deviations of the experimental points from the fitted line is a minimum.

Suppose the fitted straight line has the equation $y = mx + c$ where m is the gradient of the line and c its intercept on the y axis (Figure 4.5). If there are n pairs of (x, y) data and if it is assumed that there are random errors in the dependent variable y it can be shown that

$$m = \frac{n \sum\limits_{i=1}^{n} x_i y_i - \sum\limits_{i=1}^{n} x_i \sum\limits_{i=1}^{n} y_i}{n \sum\limits_{i=1}^{n} x_i^2 - (\sum\limits_{i=1}^{n} x_i)^2} \qquad (4.17)$$

$$c = \frac{\sum\limits_{i=1}^{n} y_i - m \sum\limits_{i=1}^{n} x_i}{n} \qquad (4.18)$$

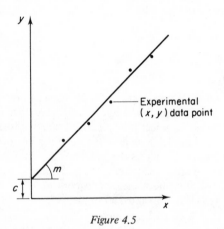

Figure 4.5

A measure of how closely the predicted straight line fits the experimental data is given by the standard deviation about the line

$$\sqrt{\left[\frac{\sum\limits_{i=1}^{n} (y_i - mx_i - c)^2}{(n-2)} \right]} \qquad (4.19)$$

Each term in the numerator of this expression is the square of the deviation of the experimental data point y_i from the fitted line.

Write a program to fit a straight line to experimental torque-twist data for a solid circular torsion specimen. Hence determine the shear modulus (G). It is necessary to specify the following data

(1) the specimen diameter (mm),
(2) the gauge length (mm) over which the angles of twist are measured,

Example 4.6 Least squares analysis of torque-twist data   49

(3) the number of data pairs, i.e. the number of load levels,
(4) each data pair, i.e. torque (kNm) and angle of twist (degrees).

In addition to the shear modulus the program should output the straight line parameters m and c and a table of the experimental values of torque and twist, the corresponding predicted values of twist and their errors.

```
EX4POINT6 15-JUN-81  11:44:07

10 PRINT "LEAST SQUARES ANALYSIS OF TORQUE-TWIST DATA"
20 PRINT "FOR A SOLID CIRCULAR TORSION SPECIMEN"
30 PRINT "--------------------------------------------------------"
40 PRINT
50 PRINT "INPUT:"
60 PRINT "SPECIMEN DIAMETER (MM)";
70 INPUT D
80 J=3.14159*D^4/32
90 PRINT "GAUGE LENGTH (MM)";
100 INPUT L
110 PRINT "NUMBER OF DATA SETS (IE LOAD LEVELS)";
120 INPUT N
130 DIM X(50),Y(50)
140 PRINT "EACH DATA SET IN PAIRS: TORQUE (KNM),TWIST (DEG)"
150 FOR I=1 TO N
160 INPUT X(I),Y(I)
170 NEXT I
180 GOSUB 1000
190 PRINT
200 PRINT "TORQUE","ACTUAL TWIST","PRED.TWIST","ERROR"
210 PRINT "(KNM)","  (DEG)","  (DEG)"
220 FOR I=1 TO N
230 Y1=M*X(I)+C
240 PRINT X(I),Y(I),Y1,Y(I)-Y1
250 NEXT I
260 PRINT
270 PRINT "STRAIGHT LINE FIT FOR 'TORQUE=M*TWIST+C'"
280 PRINT "GIVES M=";M;"AND C=";C
290 PRINT "WITH A STANDARD DEVIATION ABOUT THE LINE";S5
300 PRINT
310 G=180*L/(M/1000*3.14159*J)
320 PRINT "PREDICTED SHEAR MODULUS G IS";G;"KN/MM^2"
330 STOP
1000 REM SUBROUTINE TO PERFORM LEAST SQUARES STRAIGHT LINE FIT
1010 REM USING N SETS OF DATA PAIRS X(I) AND Y(I)
1020 REM TO GIVE SLOPE (M), INTERCEPT (C), AND STANDARD DEVIATION (S5)
1030 REM USING ADDITIONAL VARIABLE NAMES S1,S2,S3,S4
1040 S1=0
1050 S2=0
1060 S3=0
1070 S4=0
1080 S5=0
1090 FOR I=1 TO N
1100 S1=S1+X(I)
1110 S2=S2+Y(I)
1120 S3=S3+X(I)*Y(I)
1130 S4=S4+X(I)*X(I)
1140 NEXT I
1150 M=(N*S3-S1*S2)/(N*S4-S1*S1)
1160 C=(S2-M*S1)/N
1170 FOR I=1 TO N
1180 S5=S5+(Y(I)-M*X(I)-C)^2
1190 NEXT I
1200 S5=SQR(S5/(N-2))
1210 RETURN

READY
```

```
RUN


EX4POINT6  15-JUN-81   11:45:46

LEAST SQUARES ANALYSIS OF TORQUE-TWIST DATA
FOR A SOLID CIRCULAR TORSION SPECIMEN
----------------------------------------------

INPUT:
SPECIMEN DIAMETER (MM)? 50
GAUGE LENGTH (MM)? 150
NUMBER OF DATA SETS (IE LOAD LEVELS)? 11
EACH DATA SET IN PAIRS: TORQUE (KNM),TWIST (DEG)
? 0,0
? .5,.09
? 1,.19
? 1.5,.28
? 2,.36
? 2.5,.44
? 3,.53
? 3.5,.64
? 4,.72
? 4.5,.80
? 5,.90

TORQUE          ACTUAL TWIST    PRED.TWIST      ERROR
(KNM)           (DEG)           (DEG)
 0               0              3.63632E-03    -3.63632E-03
 .5              .09             .0929091      -2.90906E-03
 1               .19             .182182        7.81819E-03
 1.5             .28             .271455        8.54540E-03
 2               .36             .360727       -7.27326E-04
 2.5             .44             .45           -.0100001
 3               .53             .539273       -9.27281E-03
 3.5             .64             .628546        .0114545
 4               .72             .717818        2.18171E-03
 4.5             .8              .807091       -7.09105E-03
 5               .9              .896364        3.63624E-03

STRAIGHT LINE FIT FOR 'TORQUE=M*TWIST+C'
GIVES M= .178545 AND C= 3.63632E-03
WITH A STANDARD DEVIATION ABOUT THE LINE 7.75900E-03

PREDICTED SHEAR MODULUS G IS 78.4487 KN/MM^2

STOP AT LINE 330

READY
```

Program notes

(1) The least squares straight line fit is done in a subroutine (lines 1000 to 1210). The variable names S1, S2, S3 and S4 represent the summations required to determine the gradient (M) and intercept (C). The squares of the deviations are summed as S5 in line 1180. The standard deviation is then determined as S5 in line 1200.

(2) The predicted values of twist which correspond to the experimental values are determined (as Y1) in line 230.

(3) The shear modulus (G) is calculated in line 310 from Equation (4.7) which gives

$$G = TL/\theta J \qquad (4.20)$$

The gradient M of the fitted straight line represents θ/T with θ measured in degrees and T in kNm. Line 310 includes a conversion of θ to radians and T to kNmm. This gives a value of G in kN/mm^2.

The polar second moment of area J is calculated in line 80 using Equation (4.9).

PROBLEMS

(4.1) Example 4.1 concerns the design of a simple pressure vessel safety valve. Modify the program in lines 10 to 150 so that the range of disc diameters can be varied. The minimum, maximum and number of intervening disc diameters should be specified by 'run-time' input.

(4.2) The polar second moment of area J for a hollow circular section is given by Equation (4.10). For a very thin-walled tube Equation (4.8) gives

$$J = \pi dt \cdot (d/2)^2 \qquad (4.21)$$

where πdt is the area of the section, t the wall thickness and d a diameter.

Write a program to investigate the percentage error caused by using this expression for J if the diameter d equals

(1) the internal diameter,
(2) the external diameter,
(3) the mean diameter (i.e. the average of (1) and (2)).

The error is a function of both diameter and wall thickness. It is therefore important that the program enables these to be varied.

(4.3) Write a program to design hollow steel tubes to resist a prescribed torque. Use 'run-time' input to specify the torque, tube length and outside-to-inside diameter ratio. Examine the options of thick-walled tubes of relatively small diameter and thinner-walled tubes of larger diameter (but beware of buckling). Print the resulting diameters, the angle of twist and the mass of material used for each option. Build into the program the following properties of steel: maximum allowable shear stress = 50 N/mm^2, shear modulus = 80 kN/mm^2 and density = 7800 kg/m^3.

(4.4) The riveted joint analysis program in Example 4.2 takes no account of possible failure by shearing of the plate (failure mode (d)). Modify the program to allow for this in one of two ways. Either

(1) use 'run-time' input to specify the maximum allowable shear stress in the plate (typically half the allowable tensile stress) and the distance between rivet centre and plate end (h in Figure 4.4). Hence determine the 'plate shear' load capacity and efficiency, or

(2) determine the least load capacity governed by the other failure modes, i.e. the minimum of R2, B2 and P2 in the Example 4.2 program. Hence determine the minimum required distance from rivet centre to plate end (h in Figure 4.4) using a value for allowable plate shear stress equal to half the allowable plate tensile stress.

(4.5) For an isotropic material only two of the four elastic constants E, G, K and ν are independent. The relationships are given by Equations (4.4) and (4.6).

Write a program to calculate the other two constants if any two of them are specified.

(4.6) Application of Equation 4.7 for the torsion of circular shafts is not restricted to situations in which the torque is applied statically.

Rotating shafts are used for transmitting power. The power, which is measured in watts (W i.e. Nm/s), equals torque multiplied by the angle through which the shaft rotates per unit of time. The rotational speed is usually measured in revolutions per minute (rev/min). Hence

$$\text{Torque (in Nm)} = \frac{\text{Power (in watts)}}{\text{rev/min} \times 2\pi/60}$$

Modify the programs in Examples 4.4 and 4.5 so that the value of torque used in the analyses (T, N mm) are determined from 'run-time' input of power to be transmitted (in kW) and rotational speed (in rev/min).

(4.7) Consider a flange coupling between two sections of shaft required to transmit a specified power at a specified rotational speed. The flanges are fixed together by a number of bolts (N) at a specified pitch circle (radius R).

For design purposes it is usual to assume that the torque (T) applied to the shafts is supported in the flange coupling by uniform shear stresses in the bolts. Hence

$$T = N.\tau.\pi d^2 / 4.R$$

where d is the bolt diameter and τ is the average shear stress in each bolt. If either the number of bolts or the individual bolt diameter is specified the other can be determined. Write a program to do this.

Use 'run-time' input of power (kW) and speed (rev/min) from which the transmitted torque can be calculated. Values of the pitch circle diameter and maximum allowable shear stress must also be specified.

(4.8) Modify the program in Example 4.4 so that, in addition to designing a solid shaft, the program designs a hollow shaft of prescribed external to internal diameter ratio.

With this modification the program would give the required internal and external diameters for the hollow shaft. It is likely however that a tube of these dimensions would not be available 'off the shelf' and the shaft would have to be machined from solid material. A more useful program for the design of hollow circular shafts would use preferred hollow tube sizes. Write a program to do this using the program in Example 4.5 as a model.

(4.9) In Example 4.2 a simple riveted joint was analysed and its load capacity was determined. Using the program in that example it is possible to adjust the plate and rivet dimensions until the joint carries any specified load.

In practice, multiple rivets (or bolts) would probably be used in either a single line or in several rows (with possibly a different number in each row). Also the rivets (or bolts) would need to have a preferred diameter. A general multiple rivet (or bolt) analysis is quite complicated to program but the design of a joint with multiple in-line rivets (or bolts) is not difficult. Write such a program on the following lines.

Use 'run-time' input to specify the maximum allowable stresses in plate and rivet and the maximum load to be carried. Also input initial estimates of rivet diameter and plate thickness and width. The program should then use the failure criteria discussed in Example 4.2 in order to assess the required number of rivets — the minimum number to prevent shearing of the rivets and crushing of the plate or rivets and the maximum number of in-line rivets to prevent tearing of the plate. Hence an iterative procedure can be used whereby the plate and rivet dimensions are varied until the number of required rivets is similar according to the various failure criteria.

(4.10) Write a program to analyse experimental strain gauge data which give axial and lateral strains for a member subjected to tensile loading. Hence determine the following material properties: Young's modulus (E), Shear modulus (G) and Poisson's ratio (ν). The following data should be specified

(1) the cross-section area of the specimen (mm^2),
(2) the number of data sets, i.e. the number of load levels,
(3) each data set comprising load (kN), axial strain and lateral strain (microstrain).

Hints:
    (a) Separate straight lines must be fitted for load versus axial strain and load versus lateral strain using the least squares analysis described in Example 4.6.
    (b) Young's modulus is obtained from the gradient of the load versus axial strain line. Poisson's ratio is given by the ratio of the gradients of the two lines and shear modulus can be determined from the other two elastic constants.

A modification to this program would allow two axial strains to be specified at each load level. It is common practice to use two gauges on opposite edges of a specimen to take into account possible bending of the specimen. At each load level these two axial strains can be averaged (to eliminate the effects of bending) and then analysed in a single axial strain versus load relationship.

Chapter 5

Bending

ESSENTIAL THEORY

5.1 Representation of beams

Loads acting transversely to the plane of largest dimension cause a member to bend and a bar member subject to this loading is called a *beam*.

In order to resist these loads a beam must be supported at one or more positions along its length. The diagrammatic representation of two beams in Figure 5.1 shows a pin support which fixes position but allows rotation, a roller support which allows rotation and displacement in only one direction (e.g. horizontal) and a built-in (or encastré) support which prevents any displacement or rotation. If a beam has one end built in it is called a *cantilever*, if it has one end pinned with a roller support at the other end it is called a *simply supported* beam.

The loading on a beam may be distributed along all or part of its length either uniformly (as shown in Figure 5.1) or non-uniformly. A uniformly distributed load is measured as load per unit length, e.g. kN/m. A load applied over a length which is small compared to that of the beam may be represented as a point (or concentrated) load.

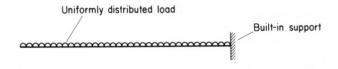

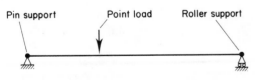

Figure 5.1

55

5.2 Reactions and fixing moments

In order that a beam as a whole is in equilibrium there are reactions and fixing moments at the supports. At both the roller and pin supports in Figure 5.1 there are just vertical reactions (there being no horizontal forces on the beam). At the built-in support of a cantilever there is a vertical reaction and a fixing moment which prevents rotation at the support.

The beams in Figure 5.1 have therefore two reactions, or a reaction and a fixing moment respectively. Their values are found from two equilibrium equations obtained by

(1) resolving forces vertically for the whole beam,
(2) taking moments about any position along the beam.

When a beam is supported such that there are more than two unknown forces (or moments) the problem is statically indeterminate and additional equations have to be found by considering displacements of the beam.

5.3 Shear force and bending moment

Not only is a beam in equilibrium as a whole but in addition, internal forces and moments maintain the static equilibrium of all parts of the beam. If an end loaded cantilever AB is hypothetically cut at C as shown in Figure 5.2, then both AC and CB must separately be in equilibrium. This internal equilibrium is maintained by *shear forces* (Q) and *bending moments* (M).

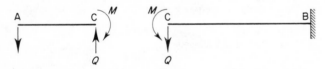

Figure 5.2

The values of Q and M at any position along the beam are obtained by considering the equilibrium of part of the beam (e.g. AC or CB). Expressed generally.

shear force (Q) is the total algebraic sum of the external forces acting to any one side of the section considered.

and

bending moment (M) is the total algebraic sum of the moments of the external forces acting to any one side of the section considered.

The sign convention for Q and M used in this book is that downward forces to the left of the section considered give positive values of Q and M.

By considering the equilibrium of a small length of a beam it can be shown that

$$Q = \frac{dM}{dx} \tag{5.1}$$

and

$$w = \frac{dQ}{dx} = \frac{d^2M}{dx^2} \tag{5.2}$$

where x is position along the beam and w is the load per unit length.

5.4 Direct stresses in beams

Bending moments cause direct stresses in a beam in the direction of its longitudinal axis. The values of these stresses can be found by considering a beam subject to pure bending. A small length of such a beam is shown in Figure 5.3.

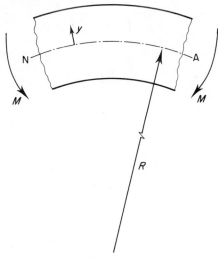

Figure 5.3

The top layers of this beam are stretched; the bottom layers are compressed. Between the top and bottom is a neutral surface, the length of which is unchanged by bending. The line of this surface along the beam is known as the *neutral axis* (NA).

Simple bending theory assumes a material that is linearly elastic with an equal Young's modulus (E) in tension and compression. It also assumes that any small length of the beam is bent into a circular arc with a radius of curvature (R) which is large compared to the cross-section dimensions.

Consideration of compatibility and the stress–strain relation shows that the longitudinal direct stress (σ) is zero at the neutral axis and varies linearly with distance y from the neutral axis.

For there to be no net horizontal force, equilibrium shows that

$$\int y\mathrm{d}A = 0 \tag{5.3}$$

where $\int y\mathrm{d}A$ is the first moment of area of the cross-section about the neutral axis. As this equals zero the neutral axis must pass through the centroid (centre of gravity) of the section.

The concepts of equilibrium, compatibility and the stress–strain relation are combined to give

$$\sigma/y = M/I = E/R \tag{5.4}$$

I represents the second moment of area of the cross-section about the neutral axis where

$$I = \int y^2\,\mathrm{d}A \tag{5.5}$$

This equation can be used to determine I for a section after having first determined the position of the neutral axis from Equation (5.3). Several commonly used cross-sections are symmetrical and have their neutral axis at mid-depth.

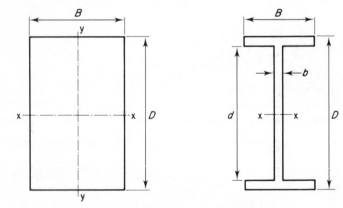

Figure 5.4

For a rectangular cross-section of depth D and breadth B (Figure 5.4)

$$I_{xx} = BD^3/12 \; ; I_{yy} = B^3D/12 \qquad (5.6)$$

For a symmetrical I-shaped section (Figure 5.4)

$$I_{xx} = BD^3/12 - (B - b)d^3/12 \qquad (5.7)$$

For a solid circular cross-section of diameter D

$$I_{NA} = \pi D^4/64 \qquad (5.8)$$

For a hollow circular cross-section of external diameter D_2 and internal diameter D_1

$$I_{NA} = \frac{\pi(D_2{}^4 - D_1{}^4)}{64} \qquad (5.9)$$

It is common to use a geometrical property of the cross-section called *section modulus* (Z) where

$$Z = I/y_{max} \qquad (5.10)$$

The second moment of area is sometimes expressed in terms of the area of the section A and its *radius of gyration r* where

$$I = Ar^2 \qquad (5.11)$$

The highest direct stress in a beam occurs at the section of maximum bending moment (M_{max}) at the surface of the beam furthest from the neutral axis (y_{max}). Therefore from Equations (5.4) and (5.10)

$$\sigma_{max} = \frac{M_{max}\, y_{max}}{I} = \frac{M_{max}}{Z} \qquad (5.12)$$

5.5 Shear stresses in beams

Shear forces cause shear stresses which are important for some types of beam (e.g. if short and deep).

By using Equation (5.4) and by considering the equilibrium of a small length of beam where the shear force is Q, the shear stress τ at any position along XX in the cross-section (Figure 5.5) is given by

$$\tau = \frac{A\bar{y}}{zI_{NA}} \qquad (5.13)$$

where z is the breadth of the beam section at XX, A is the area of the section above XX and $\bar{y}$ is the distance from the centroid of A to the

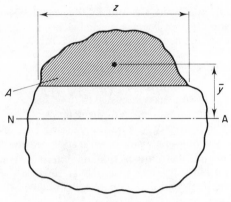

Figure 5.5

neutral axis of the cross-section. I_{NA} is the second moment of area of the complete cross-section about the netural axis.

5.6 Beam deflections

Suppose a beam has lateral deflections v which vary with position along the beam (x measured from one end). If these deflections are small the curvature of the beam at any position along its length is given by

$$\frac{1}{R} = \frac{d^2 v}{dx^2} \tag{5.14}$$

This relationship combined with Equation (5.4) gives

$$EI \frac{d^2 v}{dx^2} = M \tag{5.15}$$

If the bending moment (M) can be expressed as a function of distance along the beam (x) it is possible to obtain lateral deflections (v) by successive integration. The first integration gives slopes (dv/dx); the second integration gives deflections (v).

There are a number of other methods for determining deflections (see the references, page 00) including superposition of standard cases. Equations (5.17) give deflection expressions for a simply supported beam with a point load (W). If this load is positioned at mid-span ($a = b = L/2$) the maximum deflection occurs there with a value $WL^3/48EI$. Equations (5.23) and (5.24) give deflection expressions for loaded cantilevers. Note the product EI which occurs in all of these deflection expressions — it is called *flexural rigidity*. The stiffness of a beam is directly proportional to flexural rigidity.

Example 5.1 Shear force and bending moment distribution   61

Deflections due to shear are usually neglected. They can be significant for some types of beam, e.g. sandwich materials containing a flexible core such as foamed plastic.

5.7 Other aspects of bending

Important aspects of bending not discussed in this Chapter include

    (1) plastic bending: stresses beyond the yield strength do not cause immediate yielding of a whole beam section because the stresses are not uniformly distributed,

    (2) composite beams; different materials are used in combination, for example, steel-reinforced concrete and sandwich beams,

    (3) unsymmetrical bending,

    (4) built-in and continuous beams,

    (5) curved bars.

These topics are discussed in the references, page 13.

WORKED EXAMPLES

Example 5.1 Shear force and bending moment distribution

Write a program to tabulate the shear force and bending moment distribution across a simply supported beam with a uniformly distributed load (Figure 5.6). Use 'run-time' input of beam span (L in m) and load intensity (w in kN/m). Also specify the number of span sub-divisions which determine how many values of shear force (Q in kN) and bending moment (M in kNm) are to be printed.

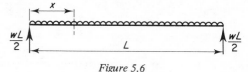

Figure 5.6

EX5POINT1 18-JUN-81   08:49:57

```
10 PRINT "SHEAR FORCE AND BENDING MOMENT DISTRIBUTION FOR A"
20 PRINT "SIMPLY SUPPORTED BEAM WITH A UNIFORMLY DISTRIBUTED LOAD"
30 PRINT "--------------------------------------------------------"
40 PRINT
50 PRINT "INPUT:"
60 PRINT "BEAM SPAN (M)";
70 INPUT L
80 PRINT "LOAD INTENSITY (KN/M)";
90 INPUT W
100 PRINT
110 PRINT "NUMBER OF SPAN SUB-DIVISIONS FOR WHICH OUTPUT REQUIRED (0 TO STOP)";
120 INPUT N
```

```
130 IF N>0 THEN 150
140 STOP
150 PRINT
160 PRINT "DISTANCE FROM","SHEAR FORCE","BENDING MOMENT"
170 PRINT "LH END (M)","   (KN)","   (KNM)"
180 FOR I=0 TO N
190 X=I*L/N
200 Q=-W*L/2+W*X
210 M=-W*L*X/2+W*X*X/2
220 PRINT X,Q,M
230 NEXT I
240 GO TO 100

READY


RUN


EX5POINT1 18-JUN-81  08:50:34

SHEAR FORCE AND BENDING MOMENT DISTRIBUTION FOR A
SIMPLY SUPPORTED BEAM WITH A UNIFORMLY DISTRIBUTED LOAD
--------------------------------------------------------

INPUT:
BEAM SPAN (M)? 4
LOAD INTENSITY (KN/M)? 5

NUMBER OF SPAN SUB-DIVISIONS FOR WHICH OUTPUT REQUIRED (0 TO STOP)? 5

DISTANCE FROM SHEAR FORCE    BENDING MOMENT
LH END (M)       (KN)           (KNM)
 0             -10           0
 .8            -6           -6.4
1.6            -2           -9.6
2.4             2           -9.6
3.2             6           -6.4
4              10            0

NUMBER OF SPAN SUB-DIVISIONS FOR WHICH OUTPUT REQUIRED (0 TO STOP)? 8

DISTANCE FROM SHEAR FORCE    BENDING MOMENT
LH END (M)       (KN)           (KNM)
 0             -10           0
 .5            -7.5         -4.375
1              -5           -7.5
1.5            -2.5         -9.375
2               0          -10
2.5             2.5         -9.375
3               5           -7.5
3.5             7.5         -4.375
4              10            0

NUMBER OF SPAN SUB-DIVISIONS FOR WHICH OUTPUT REQUIRED (0 TO STOP)? 0

STOP AT LINE 140

READY
```

Program notes

(1) In the loop between lines 180 and 230 the left-hand end of the
beam is represented by I equal to zero and the right-hand by I equal to
N. The values of I are used in line 190 to generate the distance X from
the left-hand end.

Example 5.2 Analysis of simply supported beam with point load   63

(2) Application of the definitions of shear force and bending moment from Section 5.3 to the beam shown in Figure 5.6 gives

$$Q = -\frac{1}{2} wL + wx$$

$$M = -\frac{1}{2} wL \cdot x + wx \cdot \frac{1}{2} x \qquad (5.16)$$

where the support reactions at each end of the beam are $wL/2$. These equations are represented in lines 200 and 210 respectively.

(3) The program enables the number of span sub-divisions (N) to be altered. As can be seen from the output an even number of divisions is necessary for the maximum (mid-span) bending moment to be printed. The program could be modified to give mid-span output whatever number of sub-divisions are specified.

Example 5.2 Analysis of simply supported beam with point load

Figure 5.7 shows a simply supported beam (length L) with a point load (W) positioned at a distance a from the left-hand end (or b from the right-hand end where $a + b = L$).

Show by integration of Equation (5.15) for this problem that the lateral deflection v at any distance x from the left-hand end can be expressed by

$$v = \frac{Wb}{6LEI}(-x^3 + L^2 x - b^2 x) \text{ for } x <= a$$

$$= \frac{Wb}{6LEI}(-x^3 + L^2 x - b^2 x) + \frac{W}{6EI}(x - a)^3 \text{ for } x >= a \quad (5.17)$$

Write a program to print values of shear force, bending moment and deflection at positions along the beam specified by 'run-time' input of the number of sub-divisions into which the beam is to be divided. The flexural ridigity (EI) of the beam and its length, the magnitude of the point load and its position from the left-hand end must also be specified.

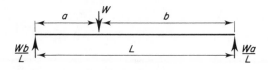

Figure 5.7

```
EX5POINT2 18-JUN-81   09:02:03

10 PRINT "SIMPLY SUPPORTED BEAM WITH SINGLE POINT LOAD"
20 PRINT "------------------------------------------------"
30 PRINT "DISTRIBUTION OF SHEAR FORCE, BENDING MOMENT AND DEFLECTION"
40 PRINT
50 PRINT "INPUT:"
60 PRINT "FLEXURAL RIGIDITY EI (KNM^2)";
70 INPUT E1
80 PRINT "BEAM SPAN (M)";
90 INPUT L
100 PRINT "DISTANCE OF POINT LOAD FROM LH END (M)";
110 INPUT A
120 IF A<L THEN 150
130 PRINT "DISTANCE MUST BE LESS THAN SPAN";L;"M"
140 GO TO 100
150 PRINT "MAGNITUDE OF LOAD (KN)";
160 INPUT W
170 B=L-A
180 R1=W*B/L
190 R2=W*A/L
200 PRINT
210 PRINT "NO OF SPAN SUB-DIVISIONS FOR WHICH OUTPUT REQUIRED (0 TO STOP)";
220 INPUT N
230 IF N>0 THEN 250
240 STOP
250 PRINT
260 PRINT "DISTANCE FROM","SHEAR FORCE","BEND. MOMENT","DEFLECTION"
270 PRINT "LH END (M)","  (KN)","   (KNM)","  (MM)"
280 FOR I=0 TO N
290 X=I*L/N
300 V=(-X^3+L*L*X-B*B*X)*W*B/6/L
310 IF X>=A THEN 350
320 Q=-R1
330 M=-R1*X
340 GO TO 410
350 IF X>A THEN 380
360 Q=0
370 GO TO 390
380 Q=R2
390 M=-R2*(L-X)
400 V=V+(X-A)^3*W/6
410 PRINT X,Q,M,V*1000/E1
420 NEXT I
430 GO TO 200

READY


RUN


EX5POINT2 18-JUN-81   09:02:51

SIMPLY SUPPORTED BEAM WITH SINGLE POINT LOAD
------------------------------------------------
DISTRIBUTION OF SHEAR FORCE, BENDING MOMENT AND DEFLECTION

INPUT:
FLEXURAL RIGIDITY EI (KNM^2)? 100
BEAM SPAN (M)? 2
DISTANCE OF POINT LOAD FROM LH END (M)? .5
MAGNITUDE OF LOAD (KN)? 2

NO OF SPAN SUB-DIVISIONS FOR WHICH OUTPUT REQUIRED (0 TO STOP)? 2
```

DISTANCE FROM LH END (M)	SHEAR FORCE (KN)	BEND. MOMENT (KNM)	DEFLECTION (MM)
0	-1.5	0	0
1	.5	-.5	2.29167
2	.5	0	0

Example 5.2 Analysis of simply supported beam with point load 65

```
NO OF SPAN SUB-DIVISIONS FOR WHICH OUTPUT REQUIRED (0 TO STOP)? 8

DISTANCE FROM SHEAR FORCE    BEND. MOMENT   DEFLECTION
LH END (M)        (KN)          (KNM)         (MM)
 0               -1.5            0             0
 .25             -1.5           -.375         1.05469
 .5               0             -.75          1.875
 .75              .5            -.625         2.27865
 1                .5            -.5           2.29167
 1.25             .5            -.375         1.99219
 1.5              .5            -.25          1.45833
 1.75             .5            -.125          .768229
 2                .5             0             0

NO OF SPAN SUB-DIVISIONS FOR WHICH OUTPUT REQUIRED (0 TO STOP)? 0

STOP AT LINE 240

READY
```

Program notes

(1) The program uses kN force units and metre length units through-out. The beam deflections are therefore calculated in metres but converted to mm for output (line 410).

(2) A check is made in line 120 to ensure that the load is not positioned further from the left-hand end than the length of the beam. If an invalid position has been specified a message is printed (line 130) and its value has to be input again.

(3) Values of the support reactions are shown in Figure 5.7. They are calculated as R1 and R2 in lines 180 and 190.

(4) The beam is sub-divided in the same way as that described in Program note (1) for Example 5.1.

(5) The common part of the deflection expressions from Equations (5.17) is determined in line 300 for any beam position. The additional term for positions to the right of the load is added in line 400 only if X exceeds A. The common EI term is not introduced until the output statement in line 410.

(6) For positions to the right of the load the shear force (Q) in the beam equals the right-hand reaction (line 380). For positions to the left of the load it equals the left-hand reaction, but with a negative sign according to the sign convention of this book (line 320).

The shear force changes between these values at the load position for which the program prints a zero value (lines 350 to 360). It can be argued that this hides the discontinuity in shear force at that position.

(7) Bending moments (M) are determined in lines 330 or 390 depending on the position along the beam. The maximum bending moment is printed only if the number of sub-divisions gives output for the load position.

66 Bending

Example 5.3 Simple beam design

Write a program to design a simply-supported beam to carry a mid-span concentrated load. For specified values of span (m), load (kN) and maximum allowable direct stress (N/mm²), the program should determine the depth (mm) of a rectangular cross-section if its breadth (mm) is specified. A wide range of breadths, with consistent values of breadth, are possible. For guidance therefore the program should output values of depth to breadth and span to depth ratios and the cross-section area.

```
EX5POINT3 18-JUN-81  09:09:44

10 PRINT "SIMPLY SUPPORTED BEAM WITH MID-SPAN POINT LOAD"
20 PRINT "STRESS BASED DESIGN FOR SOLID RECTANGULAR SECTION"
30 PRINT "DEFLECTIONS AND SHEAR NOT CONSIDERED"
40 PRINT "-------------------------------------------------------------"
50 PRINT
60 PRINT "INPUT:"
70 PRINT "BEAM SPAN (M)";
80 INPUT L
90 L=L*1000
100 PRINT "MID-SPAN CONCENTRATED LOAD (KN) - (WITH LOAD FACTOR?)";
110 INPUT W
120 W=W*1000
130 PRINT "MAX ALLOWABLE DIRECT STRESS (N/MM^2)";
140 INPUT S
150 M=W*L/4
160 Z=M/S
170 PRINT
180 PRINT "BREADTH (MM)";
190 INPUT B
200 D=SQR(6*Z/B)
210 PRINT
220 PRINT "REQUIRED BEAM DEPTH IS";D;"MM"
230 PRINT "DEPTH/BREADTH RATIO IS";D/B;" (POSSIBLE STABILITY PROBLEMS IF >'
240 PRINT "SPAN/DEPTH RATIO IS";L/D;" (SHEAR EFFECTS IMPORTANT IF <10)"
250 PRINT "CROSS-SECTION AREA IS";B*D;"MM^2"
260 PRINT
270 PRINT "DO YOU WANT TO CHANGE THE BREADTH? INPUT YES OR NO";
280 INPUT Y$
290 IF Y$="YES" THEN 170
300 STOP

READY



RUN


EX5POINT3 18-JUN-81  09:10:28

SIMPLY SUPPORTED BEAM WITH MID-SPAN POINT LOAD
STRESS BASED DESIGN FOR SOLID RECTANGULAR SECTION
DEFLECTIONS AND SHEAR NOT CONSIDERED
-------------------------------------------------------------

INPUT:
BEAM SPAN (M)? 3
MID-SPAN CONCENTRATED LOAD (KN) - (WITH LOAD FACTOR?)? 5
MAX ALLOWABLE DIRECT STRESS (N/MM^2)? 10

BREADTH (MM)? 100
```

Example 5.4 Section properties of a T beam   67

```
REQUIRED BEAM DEPTH IS 150 MM
DEPTH/BREADTH RATIO IS 1.5  (POSSIBLE STABILITY PROBLEMS IF >5)
SPAN/DEPTH RATIO IS 20  (SHEAR EFFECTS IMPORTANT IF <10)
CROSS-SECTION AREA IS 15000 MM^2

DO YOU WANT TO CHANGE THE BREADTH? INPUT YES OR NO? YES

BREADTH (MM)? 50

REQUIRED BEAM DEPTH IS 212.132 MM
DEPTH/BREADTH RATIO IS 4.24264  (POSSIBLE STABILITY PROBLEMS IF >5)
SPAN/DEPTH RATIO IS 14.1421  (SHEAR EFFECTS IMPORTANT IF <10)
CROSS-SECTION AREA IS 10606.6 MM^2

DO YOU WANT TO CHANGE THE BREADTH? INPUT YES OR NO? NO

STOP AT LINE 300

READY
```

Program notes

(1) The maximum (mid-span) bending moment (M) is determined in line 150. Hence the necessary section modulus (Z) is calculated in line 160 using Equation (5.12). Any feasible beam cross-section must have this value of section modulus.

(2) After a possible breadth has been specified in line 190 the depth is determined (line 200) using Equations (5.6 for I_{xx}) and (5.10).

(3) In lines 230 and 240 the program gives warnings of possible problems if the depth to breadth and span to depth ratios are outside certain (somewhat arbitrary) values. With these ratios borne in mind the breadth can be varied to minimise the cross-sectional area.

(4) The direct stress specified in line 140 should include a factor of safety. In addition the load input in line 120 can be factored to include possible overloading.

(5) The above program is limited in concept. It takes no account of possible deflection limits nor use of preferred sizes (see Problems (5.4) and (5.11)).

Example 5.4 Section properties of a T beam

For a T-shaped cross-section (Figure 5.8), write a program to determine the section properties: position of neutral axis, section area, second moments of area, section moduli and radii of gyration about vertical and horizontal neutral axes. Use 'run-time' input of the dimensions B, D, T_1 and T_2 in any consistent units. Compare the output with a table of section properties for a standard T beam.

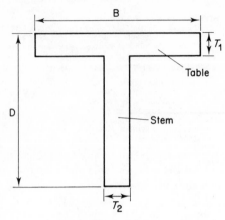

Figure 5.8

```
EX5POINT4 22-JUN-81  12:57:47

10 PRINT "SECTION PROPERTIES OF T BEAM WITH VERTICAL AXIS OF SYMMETRY"
20 PRINT "_____"
30 PRINT
40 PRINT "INPUT:"
50 PRINT "WIDTH AND DEPTH OF HORIZONTAL TABLE";
60 INPUT B,T1
70 PRINT "OVERALL DEPTH OF SECTION AND THICKNESS OF VERTICAL STEM";
80 INPUT D,T2
90 REM DETERMINE NEUTRAL AXIS
100 D1=D-T1
110 A1=B*T1
120 A2=D1*T2
130 M1=A1*T1/2
140 M2=A2*(T1+D1/2)
150 Y1=(M1+M2)/(A1+A2)
160 REM DETERMINE IXX, RX AND ZX
170 I1=B*T1^3/12+A1*(Y1-T1/2)^2
180 I2=T2*D1^3/12+A2*((T1+D1/2)-Y1)^2
190 X=I1+I2
200 R1=SQR(X/(A1+A2))
210 Z1=X/(D-Y1)
220 REM DETERMINE IYY, RY AND ZY
230 Y=T1*B^3/12+D1*T2^3/12
240 R2=SQR(Y/(A1+A2))
250 Z2=Y/B*2
260 REM OUTPUT OF PROPERTIES
270 PRINT
280 PRINT "AREA OF SECTION";A1+A2
290 PRINT "DEPTH OF NEUTRAL AXIS FROM TOP OF TABLE ";Y1
300 PRINT
310 PRINT "AXIS","I","R OF GYRATION","SECTION MODULUS"
320 PRINT "XX",X,R1,Z1
330 PRINT "YY",Y,R2,Z2
340 PRINT
350 PRINT "UNITS ARE CONSISTENT WITH INPUT DATA"

READY

RUN

EX5POINT4 22-JUN-81  12:58:34

SECTION PROPERTIES OF T BEAM WITH VERTICAL AXIS OF SYMMETRY
_____

INPUT:
WIDTH AND DEPTH OF HORIZONTAL TABLE? 150,15
OVERALL DEPTH OF SECTION AND THICKNESS OF VERTICAL STEM? 100,15
```

Example 5.5 Shear stresses in a symmetrical I beam   69

```
AREA OF SECTION 3525
DEPTH OF NEUTRAL AXIS FROM TOP OF TABLE   25.5851

AXIS            I           R OF GYRATION SECTION MODULUS
XX           2.84442E+06    28.4065        38223.8
YY           4.24266E+06    34.6928        56568.8

UNITS ARE CONSISTENT WITH INPUT DATA

READY
```

Program notes

(1) In order to determine the position of the horizontal neutral axis, the program calculates the areas of table and stem (A1 and A2 respectively) and the moments of these areas about the top of the table (M1 and M2 respectively). The sum of these moments equals the moment of the complete section area about the top of the table. The moment arm for the whole section (Y1) is the distance of the centroid (and neutral axis) from the top of the table.

(2) The second moment of area of the complete section about its horizontal neutral axis (X) is obtained by adding the second moments about this axis of the table and stem (I1 and I2 respectively). These are calculated using the parallel axis theorem

$$I_{xx} = I_{NA} + Ay^2 \qquad (5.18)$$

where I_{NA} is the second moment of an area A about its own neutral axis and I_{xx} is the second moment of area about an axis distance y from that neutral axis.

(3) The vertical neutral axis lies along the centre of the stem. The second moment of area about this axis (Y) is obtained by adding the individual second moments for table and stem using Equation (5.6).

(4) The radii of gyration about horizontal and vertical neutral axes are calculated as R1 and R2 in lines 200 and 240 using Equation (5.11). The section modulii are calculated as Z1 and Z2 in lines 210 and 250 using Equation (5.10).

(5) The lack of specified units in the program has the advantage of flexibility but it relies on the program user having an understanding of the nature of the problem.

(6) The program gives values which differ from those of standard sections because the latter have radiused corners (they also have equal stem and table thickness). The program could usefully be extended to give other section properties such as mass per unit length or it could be modified to generate the properties of a number of sections.

Example 5.5 Shear stresses in a symmetrical I beam

Write a program to determine the shear stress at any position on the vertical axis of the I-shaped beam shown in Figure 5.9. 'Run-time' input should be used to specify the shear force across the section (in kN) and the section dimensions (B, D, T_1 and T_2 in mm). The program should determine the second moment of area about the horizontal neutral axis and the average shear stress assuming the shear force is carried wholly by the web.

By specifying distances from the top of the flange (Y) the program should determine the shear stress in the flange or web (or in both if $Y = T_1$).

```
EX5POINT5  7-JUL-81  09:32:04

10 PRINT "SHEAR STRESS IN A SYMMETRICAL I BEAM"
20 PRINT "----------------------------------------"
30 PRINT
40 PRINT "INPUT:"
50 PRINT "SHEAR FORCE AT SECTION (KN)";
60 INPUT Q
70 Q=Q*1000
80 PRINT "WIDTH AND DEPTH OF EACH FLANGE (MM)";
90 INPUT B,T1
100 PRINT "OVERALL DEPTH OF SECTION AND THICKNESS OF WEB (MM)";
110 INPUT D,T2
120 I=B*D^3/12-(B-T2)*(D-2*T1)^3/12
130 PRINT
140 PRINT "SECOND MOMENT OF AREA IXX";I;"MM^4"
150 PRINT "AVERAGE SHEAR STRESS (SHEAR CARRIED BY WEB)";Q/T2/(D-2*T1);"N/MM^2"
160 PRINT
170 PRINT "INPUT DEPTH FROM TOP SURFACE AT WHICH"
180 PRINT "STRESS REQUIRED (-VE TO STOP)";
190 INPUT Y
200 IF Y>=0 THEN 220
210 STOP
220 IF Y<=D/2 THEN 240
230 Y=D-Y
240 IF Y>T1 THEN 290
250 M=B*Y*(D/2-Y/2)
260 S=M*Q/B/I
270 PRINT "FLANGE: SHEAR STRESS";S;"N/MM^2"
280 IF Y<T1 THEN 160
290 M=B*T1*(D/2-T1/2)+T2*(Y-T1)*(D/2-T1-(Y-T1)/2)
300 S=M*Q/T2/I
310 PRINT "WEB: SHEAR STRESS";S;"N/MM^2"
320 GO TO 160

READY


RUN


EX5POINT5   7-JUL-81  09:32:49

SHEAR STRESS IN A SYMMETRICAL I BEAM
----------------------------------------

INPUT:
SHEAR FORCE AT SECTION (KN)? 250
WIDTH AND DEPTH OF EACH FLANGE (MM)? 150,12
OVERALL DEPTH OF SECTION AND THICKNESS OF WEB (MM)? 300,12

SECOND MOMENT OF AREA IXX 9.57174E+07 MM^4
AVERAGE SHEAR STRESS (SHEAR CARRIED BY WEB) 75.4831 N/MM^2

INPUT DEPTH FROM TOP SURFACE AT WHICH
STRESS REQUIRED (-VE TO STOP)? 0
FLANGE: SHEAR STRESS 0 N/MM^2
```

Example 5.5 Shear stresses in a symmetrical I beam 71

```
INPUT DEPTH FROM TOP SURFACE AT WHICH
STRESS REQUIRED (-VE TO STOP)? 12
FLANGE: SHEAR STRESS 4.51329 N/MM^2
WEB: SHEAR STRESS 56.4161 N/MM^2

INPUT DEPTH FROM TOP SURFACE AT WHICH
STRESS REQUIRED (-VE TO STOP)? 75
WEB: SHEAR STRESS 73.9404 N/MM^2

INPUT DEPTH FROM TOP SURFACE AT WHICH
STRESS REQUIRED (-VE TO STOP)? 150
WEB: SHEAR STRESS 81.2862 N/MM^2

INPUT DEPTH FROM TOP SURFACE AT WHICH
STRESS REQUIRED (-VE TO STOP)? 225
WEB: SHEAR STRESS 73.9404 N/MM^2

INPUT DEPTH FROM TOP SURFACE AT WHICH
STRESS REQUIRED (-VE TO STOP)? -1

STOP AT LINE 210

READY
```

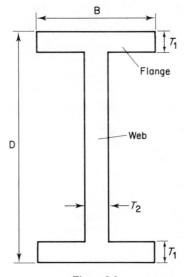

Figure 5.9

Program notes

(1) The second moment of area of the section (I) is determined in line 120 using Equation (5.7).

(2) The shear stress distribution across the vertical axis is symmetrical about the horizontal neutral axis. Values of Y greater than half the total depth (D/2) are therefore modified in lines 220 to 230 so that 'bottom half' stresses are determined from 'top half' equations.

(3) For positions in the flange (Y less than or equal to T1) the shear stress is determined in lines 250 and 260 using Equation (5.13). For positions in the web the shear stress is determined in lines 290 to 300 using the same equation. The variable M is used to represent the moment of the area above the position considered ($A\bar{y}$ in Equation (5.13)).

If Y equals T1 the program calculates the shear stress in both flange and web (neither of the IF conditions in lines 240 or 280 being satisfied).

Example 5.6 Slopes and deflections by integration

A numerical procedure can be used to integrate Equation (5.15), the governing equation for beam deflections. This method is particularly useful if the flexural rigidity (EI) varies along the length of the beam.

Write a program to integrate M/EI to give slopes and deflections for a cantilever beam using the following procedure

(1) express M/EI as a function of distance x from the built-in end using a defined function,
(2) divide the beam into N segments and calculate the step length H (equal to L/N where L is the beam length),
(3) set to zero the built-in end conditions for slope $S(0)$ and deflection $V(0)$,
(4) use the trapezium rule for numerical integration to estimate the slope (at x equal to H)

$$S(1) = \frac{dv}{dx} = \int_{i=0}^{i=1} \frac{M}{EI}\, dx \qquad (5.19)$$

where i is the station number (Figure 5.10),
(5) use the trapezium rule to estimate the deflection (at x equal to H)

$$V(1) = \int_{i=0}^{i=1} \frac{dv}{dx}\, dx \qquad (5.20)$$

(6) repeat stages (4) and (5) for subsequent segments up to the end of the beam (i.e. $i = 1$ to 2, etc.). At each station the slope (or deflection) is that at the previous station plus the integral over the segment, e.g.

$$S(2) = S(1) + \int_{i=1}^{i=2} \frac{M}{EI}\, dx \qquad (5.21)$$

and at each station the value of x increases by H.

Example 5.6 Slopes and deflections by integration 73

The program should include instructions for a potential user. Check the program using the problem of a uniform cantilever with a concentrated load at its free end.

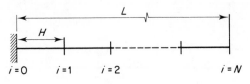

Figure 5.10

```
EX5POINT6 22-JUN-81  13:15:37
1 PRINT "CALCULATION OF SLOPES AND DEFLECTIONS OF A CANTILEVER BEAM"
2 PRINT "----------------------------------------------------------------"
3 PRINT "TO USE THIS PROGRAM YOU MUST"
4 PRINT "DELETE LINES 1 TO 9 - 'DEL 1-9'"
5 PRINT "AND               --------"
6 PRINT "DEFINE A FUNCTION FNM(X) IN LINE 10 WHICH DESCRIBES 'M/EI' AS A"
7 PRINT "FUNCTION OF L (BEAM LENGTH) AND X (DISTANCE FROM BUILT-IN END)"
8 PRINT "EG '10 DEF FNM(X)=L-X' FOR A POINT LOAD AT THE FREE END WITH W=EI=1"
9 STOP
10 PRINT "ERROR: YOU MUST DEFINE THE FUNCTION FNM(X) IN LINE 10"
20 PRINT "SLOPES AND DEFLECTIONS OF A LOADED CANTILEVER"
30 PRINT "FOR 'M/EI' FUNCTION DEFINED IN LINE 10"
40 PRINT "----------------------------------------------------"
50 PRINT
60 PRINT "INPUT LENGTH L";
70 INPUT L
80 PRINT
90 PRINT "INPUT NUMBER OF SUB-DIVISIONS (0 TO STOP)";
100 INPUT N
110 IF N>0 THEN 140
120 PRINT "'LIST 10' TO PRINT DEFINED M/EI FUNCTION"
130 STOP
140 DIM S(20),V(20),M(20)
150 S(0)=0
160 V(0)=0
170 M(0)=FNM(0)
180 H=L/N
190 PRINT
200 PRINT "DISTANCE","M/EI","SLOPE","DEFLECTION"
210 X=0
220 PRINT X,M(0),S(0),V(0)
230 FOR I=1 TO N
240 X=X+H
250 M(I)=FNM(X)
260 A=(M(I-1)+M(I))*H/2
270 S(I)=S(I-1)+A
280 B=(S(I-1)+S(I))*H/2
290 V(I)=V(I-1)+B
300 PRINT X,M(I),S(I),V(I)
310 NEXT I
320 GO TO 80

READY

RUN

EX5POINT6 22-JUN-81  13:16:33

CALCULATION OF SLOPES AND DEFLECTIONS OF A CANTILEVER BEAM
----------------------------------------------------------------
TO USE THIS PROGRAM YOU MUST
DELETE LINES 1 TO 9 - 'DEL 1-9'
AND               --------
```

```
DEFINE A FUNCTION FNM(X) IN LINE 10 WHICH DESCRIBES 'M/EI' AS A
FUNCTION OF L (BEAM LENGTH) AND X (DISTANCE FROM BUILT-IN END)
EG '10 DEF FNM(X)=L-X' FOR A POINT LOAD AT THE FREE END WITH W=EI=1

STOP AT LINE 9

READY
DEL 1-9

READY
10 DEF FNM(X)=L-X

RUN


EX5POINT6 22-JUN-81   13:17:15

SLOPES AND DEFLECTIONS OF A LOADED CANTILEVER
FOR 'M/EI' FUNCTION DEFINED IN LINE 10
---------------------------------------------------------

INPUT LENGTH L? 1

INPUT NUMBER OF SUB-DIVISIONS (0 TO STOP)? 2

DISTANCE      M/EI        SLOPE         DEFLECTION
 0            1           0             0
 .5           .5          .375          .09375
 1            0           .5            .3125

INPUT NUMBER OF SUB-DIVISIONS (0 TO STOP)? 4

DISTANCE      M/EI        SLOPE         DEFLECTION
 0            1           0             0
 .25          .75         .21875        .0273438
 .5           .5          .375          .101563
 .75          .25         .46875        .207031
 1            0           .5            .328125

INPUT NUMBER OF SUB-DIVISIONS (0 TO STOP)? 8

DISTANCE      M/EI        SLOPE         DEFLECTION
 0            1           0             0
 .125         .875        .117188       7.32422E-03
 .25          .75         .21875        .0283203
 .375         .625        .304688       .0610352
 .5           .5          .375          .103516
 .625         .375        .429688       .153809
 .75          .25         .46875        .209961
 .875         .125        .492188       .27002
 1            0           .5            .332031

INPUT NUMBER OF SUB-DIVISIONS (0 TO STOP)? 0
'LIST 10' TO PRINT DEFINED M/EI FUNCTION
```

Program notes

(1) The program output shows how the instructions are used and how, if no function is defined in line 10, a warning is printed. Because the defined function cannot be directly printed when the program is run, line 120 prints a suggestion that line 10 be listed afterwards.

(2) The function eventually used in line 10 represents an end loaded cantilever with $w = EI = 1$. As shown in Equations (5.23) the free end deflection should be 1/3 and the free end slope 1/2 for this problem.

(3) The boundary conditions of slope and deflection are set to zero in lines 150 and 160 respectively. The bending moment at the built-in end M(0) is determined in line 170 using the defined function with X set to zero.

(4) The integral in Equation (5.19) is calculated (as A) in line 260 assuming the area between the limits to be represented by a single trapezium. The integral in Equation (5.20) is calculated (as B) in line 280. The next value of X is determined in line 240 and this is used in the defined function to calculate the bending moment (line 250).

(5) The program assumes the use of consistent units.

(6) The numerical procedure can be seen as having a physical justification. In mathematical terms it is an example of the predictor—corrector method for solving ordinary differential equations.

PROBLEMS

(5. 1) Write a program in the style of Example 5.1 to tabulate the shear force (Q) and bending moment (M) distribution across a simple supported beam (length L) a mid-span concentrated load (W).
(Note: the discontinuities at mid-span in the expressions for M and Q

$$Q = -\frac{1}{2}W \quad x < = \frac{1}{2}L$$

$$= \frac{1}{2}W \quad x > = \frac{1}{2}L$$

$$M = -\frac{1}{2}Wx \quad x < = \frac{1}{2}L \qquad (5.22)$$

$$= -\frac{1}{2}Wx + W(x - \frac{1}{2}L) \quad x > = \frac{1}{2}L$$

where x is the distance from one end of the beam.)
(5. 2) Write a program to print values of shear force, bending moment and deflection at positions along a simply supported beam loaded by a number of different point loads at various positions along the beam. The program input and output should follow the style of Example 5.2.

Hint: The program can follow very closely that in Example 5.2 except that subscripted variables should be used to represent each separate load and its position. If the support reactions due to each load are represented by subscripted variables, superposition can be used to sum the individual load contributions to shear force, bending moment and deflection. Equations (5.17) give deflection expressions for any individual load.

(5. 3) Consider a cantilever beam length L with distance x measured from the free end.

For a concentrated load P at the free end

$$\frac{dv}{dx} = \frac{P}{2EI} (x^2 - L^2) \tag{5.23}$$

$$v = \frac{P}{6EI} (x^3 - 3L^2 x + 2L^3)$$

For a uniformly distributed load w

$$\frac{dv}{dx} = \frac{w}{6EI} (x^3 - L^3) \tag{5.24}$$

$$v = \frac{w}{24EI} (x^4 - 4L^3 x + 3L^4)$$

Verify these expressions for slope (dv/dx) and deflection (v) by integrating Equation (5.15).

Write a program which uses superposition of these two cases to give slopes and deflections of a cantilever beam subject to both uniform and end point loading.

Use 'run-time' input to specify the flexural rigidity $(EI$ in KNm^2), beam length (in m), load intensity (kN/m) and free end point load (kN).

The program should print deflections (in mm) and slopes (in degrees) for a number of positions along the beam, a number also specified by 'run-time' input.

(5. 4) Modify the program in Example 5.3 so that the selected beam depths are chosen from one of the preferred sizes used in Example 3.3.

(5. 5) Use the method described in Example 5.5 in order to extend the program in Example 5.4 so that shear stresses can be calculated for any position on the vertical neutral axis of a T-shaped section. The program should print stresses in both table and stem if the chosen position coincides with the intersection between these two parts of the section.

(5. 6) Extend the program in Example 5.5 so that additional 'run-time' input of bending moment gives the direct stress at any depth from the top surface.

(5. 7) Write a program similar to that in Example 5.4 to give the section properties of an I-shaped beam with unequal flanges. Extend the program to compute shear stresses in the section.

(5. 8) Modify the materials comparison program in Example 3.5 so that it compares materials on a basis of equivalent bending stiffness. Extend the program to include material costs as in Problem (3.6).

Hint: The stiffness of a beam is directly proportional to flexural rigidity (EI). Using Equation (5.6) for beams of equal breadth, equivalent bending stiffness is represented by equivalent 'Et^3' where t is the beam thickness. Modification of the program in Example 3.5 involves merely the replacement of an 'Et' equivalence by an 'Et^3' equivalence.

(5.9) Use the program in Example 5.6 to show that the free end deflection of the tapered cantilever shown in Figure 5.11 is $0.581q/EI_0$ where the load intensity varies linearly from zero at the built-in end to q at the free end.

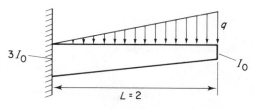

Figure 5.11

(5. 10) Write a program similar to that in Example 5.6 in order to integrate from a load intensity w first to shear force Q and then to bending moment M. The justification for this is based on Equations (5.1) and (5.2). Check the program with a simple example such as a uniformly distributed load.

The program could be extended to combine the features of the above problem and Example 5.6. Hence beam deflections could be determined directly from load intensity after four integrations.

A further modification to these programs would allow any load intensity to be specified by empirical values at each station instead of the algebraic defined function as used in Example 5.6.

(5.11) The beam design program in Example 5.3 is modest in concept. A more comprehensive program could be written in stages to include

(1) deflection as well as stress limits upon which to base the design (see Example 4.4),
(2) self weight loading by adding it after a provisional section has been selected (the section could then be checked for adequacy and modified accordingly),
(3) the use of standard section properties,
(4) additional loading and support conditions.

A subroutine-based approach would aid the writing of such a program.

Chapter 6

Complex stress and strain

ESSENTIAL THEORY

6.1 Combined bending and axial loading

Direct stresses can be superposed for linear elastic problems in which deformations are small.

Combined bending and axial loading give direct stresses

$$\sigma = P/A \pm My/I \qquad (6.1)$$

from Equations (3.1) and (5.4). The positive sign is used if the bending stress is tensile, the negative sign is used for compressive bending stresses.

6.2 Complex stress in two dimensions

Stress resultants on oblique planes and the combined effects of direct stress and shear stress (e.g. due to combined bending and torsion) are analysed by considering the equilibrium of a small element of material.

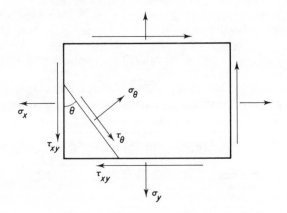

Figure 6.1

For a two-dimensional $(x - y$ plane) stress system as shown in Figure 6.1 the stresses on a plane θ are a direct stress σ_θ and a shear stress τ_θ where

$$\sigma_\theta = \frac{1}{2}(\sigma_x + \sigma_y) + \frac{1}{2}(\sigma_x - \sigma_y)\cos 2\theta + \tau_{xy} \sin 2\theta \qquad (6.2)$$

$$\tau_\theta = \frac{1}{2}(\sigma_x - \sigma_y)\sin 2\theta - \tau_{xy} \cos 2\theta \qquad (6.3)$$

By evaluating $d\sigma_\theta/d\theta = 0$ it is found that maximum and minimum values of direct stress σ_θ occur on planes $90°$ apart at angles θ_p where

$$\tan 2\theta_p = \frac{2\tau_{xy}}{(\sigma_x - \sigma_y)} \qquad (6.4)$$

These are called *principal planes* and the corresponding direct stresses (σ_1, σ_2) are called *principal stresses*. By substituting Equation (6.4) into Equation (6.2) it is found that

$$\sigma_1 = \frac{(\sigma_x + \sigma_y)}{2} + \sqrt{\left[\left(\frac{\sigma_x - \sigma_y}{2}\right)^2 + \tau^2{}_{xy}\right]}$$

$$\sigma_2 = \frac{(\sigma_x + \sigma_y)}{2} - \sqrt{\left[\left(\frac{\sigma_x - \sigma_y}{2}\right)^2 + \tau^2{}_{xy}\right]} \qquad (6.5)$$

The shear stress is zero on the principal planes and has a maximum value

$$\tau_{max} = \frac{(\sigma_1 - \sigma_2)}{2} = \sqrt{\left[\left(\frac{\sigma_x - \sigma_y}{2}\right)^2 + \tau^2{}_{xy}\right]} \qquad (6.6)$$

on planes at $45°$ to the principal planes.

6.3 Mohr's (stress) circle

The variation of stress with direction can be represented by points on the circumference of a circle known as Mohr's circle (Figure 6.2).

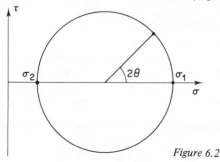

Figure 6.2

(Note: angles on this circle are double those in space. The two ends of the horizontal diameter represent the principal planes which are 90° apart in space.)

Mohr's circle can be constructed if direct and shear stress components are known for two planes at right angles.

6.4 Complex strain in two dimensions

Similar equations to those shown above can be derived for two-dimensional strain relationships with ϵ_x replacing σ_x, ϵ_y replacing σ_y and $\gamma/2$ replacing τ_{xy}.

For example at an angle to the x-direction there is a direct strain ϵ_θ given by

$$\epsilon_\theta = \frac{1}{2}(\epsilon_x + \epsilon_y) + \frac{1}{2}(\epsilon_x - \epsilon_y)\cos 2\theta + \frac{1}{2}\gamma\sin 2\theta \qquad (6.7)$$

and a shear strain γ_θ given by

$$\frac{1}{2}\gamma_\theta = \frac{1}{2}(\epsilon_x - \epsilon_y)\sin 2\theta - \frac{1}{2}\gamma\cos 2\theta \qquad (6.8)$$

Mohr's strain circle is similar to the stress circle shown in Figure 6.2 but with ϵ replacing σ and $\gamma/2$ replacing τ.

Principal stresses (σ_1 and σ_2) can be derived from principal strains (ϵ_1 and ϵ_2) by solving the Hooke's law relationships in Chapter 3 (Equations (3.4) with x replaced by 1, y by 2 and σ_z equal to zero). Hence

$$\sigma_1 = \frac{E}{(1-\nu^2)}(\epsilon_1 + \nu\epsilon_2)$$

$$\sigma_2 = \frac{E}{(1-\nu^2)}(\epsilon_2 + \nu\epsilon_1) \qquad (6.9)$$

6.5 Three-dimensional stress systems

In a three-dimensional stress system there are three principal stresses σ_1, σ_2 and σ_3 in mutually perpendicular directions. Figure 6.3 shows the Mohr's circles for a typical three-dimensional state of stress.

The shear stress is maximum at 45° to the directions of maximum principal stress (σ_1) and minimum principal stress (σ_3). Its value is given by

$$\tau_{max} = \frac{1}{2}(\sigma_1 - \sigma_3) \qquad (6.10)$$

Example 6.1 Manual iterative design of a hollow box beam   81

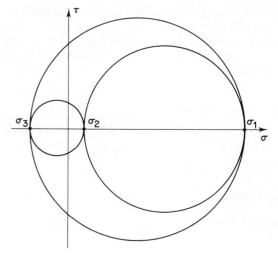

Figure 6.3

WORKED EXAMPLES

Example 6.1 Manual iterative design of a hollow box beam

Consider a square, hollow box section (shown in Figure 6.4) subjected
to combined bending and axial loading.

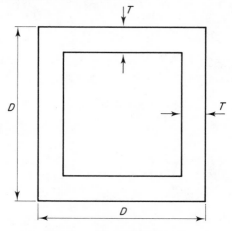

Figure 6.4

Write a program to design such a member using an allowable direct
stress limit. Assume this limit is the same in tension and compression
and neglect (but be aware of) possible limitations due to buckling and

shear. Because the equations are difficult to solve directly use a 'manual iterative procedure' as follows.

For a specified value of wall thickness T print the maximum direct stress for various values of the outside dimension D. Vary D, starting with low values, until the maximum direct stress equals the maximum allowable direct stress.

Use the program to design a section to withstand a maximum axial load of 20 kN and a bending moment of 15 kNm if the maximum allowable direct stress is 100 N/mm^2. The ratio of outside dimension (D) to wall thickness (T) should not exceed 20.

```
EX6POINT1 22-JUN-81  13:21:51

10 PRINT "ITERATIVE DESIGN OF SQUARE HOLLOW BOX BEAMS SUBJECT TO"
20 PRINT "AXIAL LOADS AND BENDING MOMENTS (BUCKLING NOT CONSIDERED)"
30 PRINT "-----------------------------------------------------------"
40 PRINT
50 PRINT "INPUT:"
60 PRINT "MAXIMUM AXIAL LOAD (KN)";
70 INPUT P
80 P=P*1000
90 PRINT "MAXIMUM BENDING MOMENT (KNM)";
100 INPUT M
110 M=M*1.00000E+06
120 PRINT
130 PRINT "WALL THICKNESS T (MM)";
140 INPUT T
150 PRINT
160 PRINT "INPUT OUTSIDE DIMENSIONS D UNTIL DIRECT STRESS LESS THAN ALLOWABLE"
170 PRINT "VALUE (0 TO STOP, -VE TO CHANGE WALL THICKNESS):"
175 PRINT "START WITH LOW D'S - IS D/T TOO LARGE (BUCKLING,SHEAR)?"
180 PRINT
190 PRINT "OUTSIDE DIMENSION D (MM)";
200 INPUT D
210 IF D<0 THEN 120
220 IF D>0 THEN 240
230 STOP
240 A=2*D*T+2*(D-2*T)*T
250 I=D^4/12-(D-2*T)^4/12
260 S=P/A+M/I*D/2
270 PRINT "MAXIMUM DIRECT STRESS";S;"N/MM^2","SECTION AREA";A;"MM^2"
280 GO TO 180

READY


RUN


EX6POINT1 22-JUN-81  13:22:40

ITERATIVE DESIGN OF SQUARE HOLLOW BOX BEAMS SUBJECT TO
AXIAL LOADS AND BENDING MOMENTS (BUCKLING NOT CONSIDERED)
-----------------------------------------------------------

INPUT:
MAXIMUM AXIAL LOAD (KN)? 20
MAXIMUM BENDING MOMENT (KNM)? 15

WALL THICKNESS T (MM)? 10

INPUT OUTSIDE DIMENSIONS D UNTIL DIRECT STRESS LESS THAN ALLOWABLE
VALUE (0 TO STOP, -VE TO CHANGE WALL THICKNESS):
START WITH LOW D'S - IS D/T TOO LARGE (BUCKLING,SHEAR)?
```

Example 6.1 Manual iterative design of a hollow box beam   83

```
OUTSIDE DIMENSION D (MM)? 50
MAXIMUM DIRECT STRESS 839.706 N/MM^2          SECTION AREA 1600 MM^2

OUTSIDE DIMENSION D (MM)? 100
MAXIMUM DIRECT STRESS 157.995 N/MM^2          SECTION AREA 3600 MM^2

OUTSIDE DIMENSION D (MM)? 150
MAXIMUM DIRECT STRESS 64.7571 N/MM^2          SECTION AREA 5600 MM^2

OUTSIDE DIMENSION D (MM)? 125
MAXIMUM DIRECT STRESS 96.1171 N/MM^2          SECTION AREA 4600 MM^2

OUTSIDE DIMENSION D (MM)? -1

WALL THICKNESS T (MM)? 8

INPUT OUTSIDE DIMENSIONS D UNTIL DIRECT STRESS LESS THAN ALLOWABLE
VALUE (0 TO STOP, -VE TO CHANGE WALL THICKNESS):
START WITH LOW D'S - IS D/T TOO LARGE (BUCKLING,SHEAR)?

OUTSIDE DIMENSION D (MM)? 100
MAXIMUM DIRECT STRESS 186.03 N/MM^2           SECTION AREA 2944 MM^2

OUTSIDE DIMENSION D (MM)? 150
MAXIMUM DIRECT STRESS 77.838 N/MM^2           SECTION AREA 4544 MM^2

OUTSIDE DIMENSION D (MM)? 130
MAXIMUM DIRECT STRESS 105.368 N/MM^2          SECTION AREA 3904 MM^2

OUTSIDE DIMENSION D (MM)? 135
MAXIMUM DIRECT STRESS 97.2348 N/MM^2          SECTION AREA 4064 MM^2

OUTSIDE DIMENSION D (MM)? 0

STOP AT LINE 230

READY
```

Program notes

(1) The program is written so that the input of the outside dimension D controls the progress of the analysis (lines 160 to 230). A zero value of D stops the run, a negative value allows the wall thickness to be changed.

(2) The maximum direct stress in the section is calculated as S in line 260 using Equation (6.1). As written the program does not distinguish between tensile and compressive axial loads or bending stresses. The value of S is always the direct stress of largest magnitude.

(3) The area of the section (A) is determined in line 240. The second moment of area (I) is determined in line 250 using Equation (5.6) — this equation being equally applicable to hollow box sections.

(4) The program output shows how the values of D are changed until the maximum direct stress approximately equals the allowable value. The wall thickness is changed in order to minimise the section area (and therefore its weight and probably its cost). The specified D/T ratio is not exceeded by this design.

Example 6.2 Automatic iterative design of a simple beam

Consider a beam of solid rectangular cross-section subject to combined bending and axial loading. If the beam breadth is 100 mm and the maximum allowable direct stress is 10 N/mm^2, use Equations (6.1) and (5.6) to calculate the necessary depth of beam to withstand an axial load of 20 kN and a maximum bending moment of 15 kNm.

As an exercise, write a program to solve this problem in the style of that in Example 6.1. However, instead of performing a manual iteration to find the beam depth, write the program so that it performs the iteration automatically. The iteration should stop when the actual maximum direct stress in the beam is within 0.1% of the allowable stress.

```
EX6POINT2 22-JUN-81  13:31:48

10 PRINT "ITERATIVE DESIGN OF RECTANGULAR SECTION BEAMS SUBJECT TO"
20 PRINT "AXIAL LOADS AND BENDING MOMENTS (BUCKLING NOT CONSIDERED)"
30 PRINT "-------------------------------------------------------------"
40 PRINT
50 PRINT "INPUT:"
60 PRINT "MAXIMUM AXIAL LOAD (KN)";
70 INPUT P
80 P=P*1000
90 PRINT "MAXIMUM BENDING MOMENT (KNM)";
100 INPUT M
110 M=M*1.00000E+06
120 PRINT "MAXIMUM ALLOWABLE DIRECT STRESS (N/MM^2)";
130 INPUT S1
140 PRINT
150 PRINT "BEAM WIDTH (MM)";
160 INPUT B
170 PRINT
180 REM ITERATION TO FIND BEAM DEPTH D
190 D=B/100 \ REM INITIAL (LOW) ESTIMATE OF D
200 D1=B/2 \ REM INCREMENT FOR INCREASING D
210 FOR C=1 TO 50
220 A=B*D
230 I=B*D^3/12
240 S=P/A+M/I*D/2
250 IF ABS((S-S1)/S1)<1.00000E-03 THEN 340 \ REM CONVERGENCE TEST
260 IF S<S1 THEN 290
270 D=D+D1 \ REM STRESS TOO HIGH - INCREASE D
280 GO TO 310
290 D=D-D1 \ REM STRESS TOO LOW - DECREASE D
300 D1=D1/5 \ REM CHANGE INCREMENT SIZE
310 NEXT C
320 PRINT "SOLUTION HAS NOT CONVERGED AFTER";C;"ITERATIONS"
330 GO TO 350
340 PRINT "AFTER";C;"ITERATIONS: BEAM DEPTH IS";D;"MM"
350 PRINT
360 PRINT "DO YOU WANT TO CHANGE THE BREADTH? INPUT YES OR NO";
370 INPUT Y$
380 IF Y$="YES" THEN 140
390 STOP

READY

RUN

EX6POINT2 22-JUN-81  13:32:41

ITERATIVE DESIGN OF RECTANGULAR SECTION BEAMS SUBJECT TO
AXIAL LOADS AND BENDING MOMENTS (BUCKLING NOT CONSIDERED)
-------------------------------------------------------------
```

Example 6.2 Automatic iterative design of a simple beam   85

```
INPUT:
MAXIMUM AXIAL LOAD (KN)? 20
MAXIMUM BENDING MOMENT (KNM)? 15
MAXIMUM ALLOWABLE DIRECT STRESS (N/MM^2)? 10

BEAM WIDTH (MM)? 100

AFTER 20 ITERATIONS: BEAM DEPTH IS 310.2 MM

DO YOU WANT TO CHANGE THE BREADTH? INPUT YES OR NO? NO

STOP AT LINE 390

READY
```

Program notes

(1) With the values of P, M, B and σ specified above, Equations (6.1) and (5.6) give a quadratic in D, the positive root of which is 310(mm) for the above problem.

(2) The program listing contains descriptive comments starting with \REM. The ability to include multiple statement lines or comments on the same lines as other program statements is a useful facility available on some computers.

(3) The maximum direct stress (S) in the beam is calculated in line 240 using Equation (6.1). The second moment of area (I) is determined from Equation (5.6) in line 230.

(4) The iterative procedure is as follows

  (a) an initial estimate is made of the beam depth D (line 190) and an increment (D1) for increasing D (line 200)

  (b) the maximum direct stress (S) is found using this value of D (line 240),

  (c) this maximum stress is compared with the allowable value (S1) to check whether the difference is less than 0.1% of S1 (line 250),

  (d) if the stress is too high the value of D is increased by the increment D1 (line 270) and the maximum stress is recalculated,

  (e) if the stress is too low the value of D is decreased by the increment (line 290). The increment size itself is then decreased (line 300) and the maximum stress is recalculated.

(5) If the value of D do not converge within 50 cycles of iteration (C) a warning message is printed (line 320). The program cannot therefore become 'stuck' in an infinite loop.

(6) Particular fixed values are set in the program for the initial estimate of D (line 190), the initial increment size (line 200), the degree by which this increment size is reduced (line 300), the convergence tolerance (line 250) and the maximum number of iterations (line 210).

(7) The manual iterative technique in Example 6.1 and the automatic

technique described above are simple methods applicable to a wide range of problems. There are, of course, more formal methods of numerical mathematics which can be used to find roots of equations.

Example 6.3 Analysis of complex stresses

Write a program to determine the direct and shear stress components on oblique planes for any specified values of the Cartesian stress components σ_x, σ_y and σ_{xy}. Print the resolved stresses on planes at $15°$ intervals from $0°$ to $90°$ to the direction of the τ_{xy} component. Determine also the principal stresses, the maximum shear stress and their orientations.

Use the program to study the following states of stress: uniaxial and biaxial tension and pure torsion. Draw a Mohr's circle for each of these stress states.

```
EX6POINT3 22-JUN-81  13:50:28

10 PRINT "2D ANALYSIS OF STRESSES ON OBLIQUE PLANES"
20 PRINT "----------------------------------------------"
30 PRINT
40 PRINT "INPUT CARTESIAN STRESS COMPONENTS:"
50 PRINT "DIRECT STRESS SIGX";
60 INPUT X
70 PRINT "DIRECT STRESS SIGY";
80 INPUT Y
90 PRINT "SHEAR STRESS TAUXY";
100 INPUT T
110 PRINT
120 PRINT "ANGLE"," STRESS COMPONENTS"
130 PRINT "(DEG)","DIRECT","SHEAR"
140 FOR A1=0 TO 90 STEP 15
150 A=A1*3.14159/180
160 R1=(X+Y)/2+(X-Y)/2*COS(2*A)+T*SIN(2*A)
170 R2=(X-Y)/2*SIN(2*A)-T*COS(2*A)
180 PRINT A1,R1,R2
190 NEXT A1
200 PRINT
210 X9=X
220 Y9=Y
230 T9=T
240 GOSUB 1000
250 PRINT "PRINCIPAL STRESSES:"
260 PRINT "MAXIMUM: SIG1 IS ";P1;" AT ANGLE";A0;"DEG TO SIGX"
270 PRINT "MINIMUM: SIG2 IS ";P2
280 PRINT "MAX SHEAR STRESS IS ";(P1-P2)/2;" AT ANGLE";A0+45;"DEG TO SIGX"
290 PRINT
300 PRINT "DO YOU WISH TO ANALYSE ANOTHER STATE OF STRESS?"
310 PRINT "INPUT YES OR NO";
320 INPUT Y$
330 IF Y$="YES" THEN 30
340 STOP
1000 REM SUBROUTINE TO DETERMINE PRINCIPAL STRESSES (P1 AND P2) AND
1010 REM ANGLE A0 FROM SIGX (X9), SIGY (Y9) AND TAUXY (T9)
1020 P1=(Y9+X9)/2+SQR(((Y9-X9)/2)^2+T9*T9)
1030 P2=(Y9+X9)/2-SQR(((Y9-X9)/2)^2+T9*T9)
1040 IF Y9=X9 THEN 1080
1050 A0=ATN(-2*T9/(Y9-X9))/2
1060 A0=A0*180/3.14159
1070 GO TO 1090
1080 A0=0
1090 RETURN

READY
```

Example 6.3 Analysis of complex stresses   87

```
RUN


EX6POINT3 22-JUN-81  13:51:24

2D ANALYSIS OF STRESSES ON OBLIQUE PLANES
-----------------------------------------------

INPUT CARTESIAN STRESS COMPONENTS:
DIRECT STRESS SIGX? 50
DIRECT STRESS SIGY? 0
SHEAR STRESS TAUXY? 0

ANGLE           STRESS COMPONENTS
(DEG)           DIRECT          SHEAR
 0              50              0
 15             46.6506         12.5
 30             37.5            21.6506
 45             25              25
 60             12.5            21.6507
 75             3.34939         12.5
 90             -3.81470E-06    6.55387E-05

PRINCIPAL STRESSES:
MAXIMUM: SIG1 IS  50  AT ANGLE 0 DEG TO SIGX
MINIMUM: SIG2 IS  0
MAX SHEAR STRESS IS  25  AT ANGLE 45 DEG TO SIGX

DO YOU WISH TO ANALYSE ANOTHER STATE OF STRESS?
INPUT YES OR NO? YES

INPUT CARTESIAN STRESS COMPONENTS:
DIRECT STRESS SIGX? 50
DIRECT STRESS SIGY? 50
SHEAR STRESS TAUXY? 0

ANGLE           STRESS COMPONENTS
(DEG)           DIRECT          SHEAR
 0              50              0
 15             50              0
 30             50              0
 45             50              0
 60             50              0
 75             50              0
 90             50              0

PRINCIPAL STRESSES:
MAXIMUM: SIG1 IS  50  AT ANGLE 0 DEG TO SIGX
MINIMUM: SIG2 IS  50
MAX SHEAR STRESS IS  0  AT ANGLE 45 DEG TO SIGX

DO YOU WISH TO ANALYSE ANOTHER STATE OF STRESS?
INPUT YES OR NO? YES

INPUT CARTESIAN STRESS COMPONENTS:
DIRECT STRESS SIGX? 0
DIRECT STRESS SIGY? 0
SHEAR STRESS TAUXY? 50

ANGLE           STRESS COMPONENTS
(DEG)           DIRECT          SHEAR
 0              0               -50
 15             25              -43.3013
 30             43.3013         -25
 45             50              -6.55387E-05
 60             43.3013         24.9999
 75             25.0001         43.3012
 90             1.31077E-04     50

PRINCIPAL STRESSES:
MAXIMUM: SIG1 IS  50  AT ANGLE 0 DEG TO SIGX
```

```
MINIMUM: SIG2 IS -50
MAX SHEAR STRESS IS  50  AT ANGLE 45 DEG TO SIGX

DO YOU WISH TO ANALYSE ANOTHER STATE OF STRESS?
INPUT YES OR NO? NO

STOP AT LINE 340

READY
```

Program notes

(1) The direct stress (R1) and shear stress (R2) components on an oblique plane are calculated in lines 160 and 170 using Equations (6.2) and (6.3) respectively. The oblique plane angle θ measured from the σ_x direction is represented by A1 in degrees and A in radians.

(2) The principal stresses are determined in a subroutine (lines 1000 to 1090) which can be easily appended to other programs (see Example 7.2). For that reason less commonly used variable names (X9, Y9, T9, etc.) are used and the input data has to be copied to these variables (lines 210 to 230) before the subroutine is called.

(3) The subroutine uses Equation (6.5) to determine the principal stresses (P1 and P2) and Equation (6.4) to calculate the angle (A0 in degrees) between the σ_1 (P1) and σ_x directions. Line 1040 is necessary because the computer cannot handle the inifinity caused by X9=Y9 (the angle A0 is zero in this case).

(4) The maximum shear stress is calculated in line 280 from Equation (6.6), its orientation being 45° from the direction of maximum principal stress.

(5) Figure 6.5 shows the Mohr's circle representations of simple tension and pure torsion. Biaxial tension gives a uniform direct stress and zero shear stress on all oblique planes – its Mohr's circle has zero diameter.

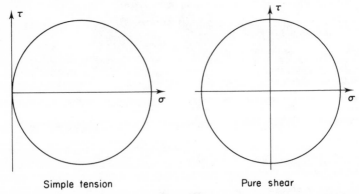

Simple tension   Pure shear

Figure 6.5

Example 6.4 Principal stresses in a beam 89

Example 6.4 Principal stresses in a beam

Write a program to determine the direct (σ_x) and shear (τ_{xy}) stresses and the resulting principal stresses in a simply supported rectangular cross-section beam subjected to a uniformly distributed load. Print the stresses (using ten sub-divisions through the beam thickness) at a support, quarter-span and mid-span.

Use the program to demonstrate the relative unimportance of shear stresses except in short, very deep beams.

```
EX6POINT4  7-JUL-81  09:42:07

10 PRINT "SIMPLY SUPPORTED RECTANGULAR CROSS-SECTION BEAM WITH UNIFORMLY"
20 PRINT "DISTRIBUTED LOAD - STRESSES ACROSS SECTION AT X FROM LH END"
30 PRINT "----------------------------------------------------------------"
40 PRINT
50 PRINT "INPUT:"
60 PRINT "BREADTH (MM)";
70 INPUT B
80 PRINT "DEPTH (MM)";
90 INPUT D
100 I=B*D^3/12
110 PRINT "SPAN (M)";
120 INPUT L
130 L=L*1000
140 PRINT "LOAD PER UNIT LENGTH (KN/M)";
150 INPUT W
160 PRINT
170 FOR I1=0 TO 2
180 X=I1*L/4
190 Q=-W*L/2+W*X
200 M=-W*L*X/2+W*X*X/2
210 PRINT "X=";X/1000;"M, BENDING MOMENT=";M/1.00000E+06;"KNM, SHEAR FORCE=";
215 PRINT Q/1000;"KN"
220 PRINT
230 PRINT "Y","SIGX","TAUXY","SIG1","SIG2"
240 PRINT "(MM)","(N/MM^2)","(N/MM^2)","(N/MM^2)","(N/MM^2)"
250 FOR I2=5 TO -5 STEP -1
260 Y=I2*D/10
270 S=M*Y/I
280 T=Q*(D*D/4-Y*Y)/2/I
290 S1=S/2+SQR(S*S/4+T*T)
300 S2=S/2-SQR(S*S/4+T*T)
310 PRINT Y,S,T,S1,S2
320 NEXT I2
330 PRINT
340 NEXT I1

READY


RUN


EX6POINT4  7-JUL-81  09:42:51

SIMPLY SUPPORTED RECTANGULAR CROSS-SECTION BEAM WITH UNIFORMLY
DISTRIBUTED LOAD - STRESSES ACROSS SECTION AT X FROM LH END
----------------------------------------------------------------

INPUT:
BREADTH (MM)? 50
DEPTH (MM)? 100
SPAN (M)? 2
LOAD PER UNIT LENGTH (KN/M)? 2

X= 0 M, BENDING MOMENT= 0 KNM, SHEAR FORCE=-2 KN
```

Y	SIGX	TAUXY	SIG1	SIG2
(MM)	(N/MM^2)	(N/MM^2)	(N/MM^2)	(N/MM^2)
50	0	0	0	0
40	0	-.216	.216	-.216
30	0	-.384	.384	-.384
20	0	-.504	.504	-.504
10	0	-.576	.576	-.576
0	0	-.6	.6	-.6
-10	0	-.576	.576	-.576
-20	0	-.504	.504	-.504
-30	0	-.384	.384	-.384
-40	0	-.216	.216	-.216
-50	0	0	0	0

X= .5 M, BENDING MOMENT=-.75 KNM, SHEAR FORCE=-1 KN

Y	SIGX	TAUXY	SIG1	SIG2
(MM)	(N/MM^2)	(N/MM^2)	(N/MM^2)	(N/MM^2)
50	-9	0	0	-9
40	-7.2	-.108	1.61982E-03	-7.20162
30	-5.4	-.192	6.81806E-03	-5.40682
20	-3.6	-.252	.0175544	-3.61755
10	-1.8	-.288	.0449572	-1.84496
0	0	-.3	.3	-.3
-10	1.8	-.288	1.84496	-.0449572
-20	3.6	-.252	3.61755	-.0175544
-30	5.4	-.192	5.40682	-6.81806E-03
-40	7.2	-.108	7.20162	-1.61982E-03
-50	9	0	9	0

X= 1 M, BENDING MOMENT=-1 KNM, SHEAR FORCE= 0 KN

Y	SIGX	TAUXY	SIG1	SIG2
(MM)	(N/MM^2)	(N/MM^2)	(N/MM^2)	(N/MM^2)
50	-12	0	0	-12
40	-9.6	0	0	-9.6
30	-7.2	0	0	-7.2
20	-4.8	0	0	-4.8
10	-2.4	0	0	-2.4
0	0	0	0	0
-10	2.4	0	2.4	0
-20	4.8	0	4.8	0
-30	7.2	0	7.2	0
-40	9.6	0	9.6	0
-50	12	0	12	0

Program notes

(1) The data are specified in their most natural units but are immediately converted to newton and millimetre units for calculation purposes. Where necessary the units are reconverted for output (line 210).

(2) The shear stress is calculated as T in line 280 using Equation (5.13) with $A = B(D/2 - Y)$, $\bar{y} = (D/2 + Y)/2$ and $z = B$. Check the validity of the above equations and the resulting expression for shear stress in line 280.

(3) The analysis in this Example assumes zero direct stress (σ_y) in the vertical direction. This is not strictly valid because σ_y must equal the load intensity at one surface. This error, which is small, does not occur when a full elasticity analysis is used.

Example 6.5 Strain gauge rosette analysis 91

The sum of direct stresses at a point is an invariant. Hence, as can be seen from the program output

$$\sigma_1 + \sigma_2 = \sigma_x + \sigma_y = \sigma_x \text{ as } \sigma_y \text{ is zero}$$

Example 6.5 Strain gauge rosette analysis

A strain gauge measures direct strain. Three such gauges in different directions give three direct strains from which the complete two-dimensional state of strain (and hence stress) can be determined. The three guages, called a rosette, give average strains over the area they cover. Ideally the gauges should be small enough for the strains (and stresses) to be reasonably uniform over this area.

Write a program to determine the principal strain magnitudes and directions for any strain gauge rosette. Determine also the principal stresses for prescribed values of Young's modulus and Poisson's ratio. The relevant theory is outlined below.

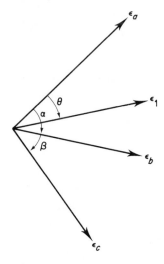

Figure 6.6

Figure 6.6 shows the notation for the three measured strain gauge readings ϵ_a, ϵ_b and ϵ_c and their relative orientations α and β. The direction (θ) and the magnitude of the maximum principal strain (ϵ_1) are unknowns to be found by the following analysis. The minimum principal strain ϵ_2 is also unknown.

Working from the principal state of strain, Equation (6.7) can be written for each gauge. Hence with

$$\epsilon_x = \epsilon_1 \ , \epsilon_y = \epsilon_2 , \gamma = 0$$

$$\epsilon_a = \frac{1}{2}(\epsilon_1 + \epsilon_2) + \frac{1}{2}(\epsilon_1 - \epsilon_2)\cos2\theta \qquad (6.11)$$

$$\epsilon_b = \frac{1}{2}(\epsilon_1 + \epsilon_2) + \frac{1}{2}(\epsilon_1 - \epsilon_2)\cos2(\theta - \alpha) \qquad (6.12)$$

$$\epsilon_c = \frac{1}{2}(\epsilon_1 + \epsilon_2) + \frac{1}{2}(\epsilon_1 - \epsilon_2)\cos2(\theta - (\alpha + \beta)) \qquad (6.13)$$

By forming $\epsilon_b - \epsilon_a$ and $\epsilon_c - \epsilon_a$ and dividing the resulting equations an expression for θ can be derived in the form

$$\tan 2\theta = \frac{\sin(\alpha + \beta) - F\sin\alpha}{\cos(\alpha + \beta) - F\cos\alpha} \qquad (6.14)$$

where

$$F = \frac{(\epsilon_c - \epsilon_a)\sin\alpha}{(\epsilon_b - \epsilon_a)\sin(\alpha + \beta)} \qquad (6.15)$$

Equations (6.11) and (6.12) can be solved to give

$$\epsilon_1 - \epsilon_2 = Y = \frac{2(\epsilon_b - \epsilon_a)}{[\cos2(\theta - \alpha) - \cos2\theta]} \qquad (6.16)$$

and

$$\epsilon_1 + \epsilon_2 = X = 2\epsilon_a - Y\cos2\theta \qquad (6.17)$$

Hence

$$\epsilon_1 = \frac{1}{2}(X + Y) \text{ and } \epsilon_2 = \frac{1}{2}(X - Y) \qquad (6.18)$$

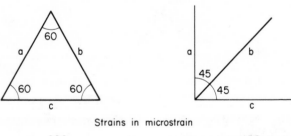

Strains in microstrain

a	200		a	150
b	-50		b	430
c	-300		c	-310

Figure 6.7

Example 6.5 Strain gauge rosette analysis   93

Verify the derivation of these equations and evaluate them in your program. The equations are valid for closed and open rosettes with the angles between gauges either clockwise or anticlockwise. The angle θ represents the angle between ϵ_1 and ϵ_a in the same direction (i.e. clockwise or anticlockwise) as the angles between the gauges. A negative value represents the opposite direction.

Use a program to analyse the two rosettes shown in Figures 6.7. For the left-hand rosette determine the stresses if the gauges are being used on a steel component.

```
EX6POINT5 22-JUN-81  15:20:37

10 PRINT "STRAIN GAUGE ROSETTE ANALYSIS"
20 PRINT "-------------------------------"
30 PRINT
40 PRINT "INPUT:"
50 PRINT "STRAINS FOR GAUGES A,B AND C (MICROSTRAIN)";
60 INPUT A,B,C
70 PRINT "ANGLES (DEG) BETWEEN A & B AND B & C";
80 INPUT A1,B1
90 PRINT
100 A1=A1*3.14159/180
110 B1=B1*3.14159/180
120 C1=A1+B1
130 F=(C-A)*SIN(A1)/(B-A)/SIN(C1)
140 T2=(SIN(C1)-F*SIN(A1))/(COS(C1)-F*COS(A1))
150 T2=ATN(T2)
160 Y=2*(B-A)/(COS(T2-2*A1)-COS(T2))
170 X=2*A-Y*COS(T2)
180 T1=T2*90/3.14159
190 E1=(X+Y)/2
200 E2=(X-Y)/2
210 IF E1>=E2 THEN 240
220 T2=T2+3.14159
230 GO TO 160
240 PRINT "PRINCIPAL STRAINS",E1,E2;" MICROSTRAIN"
250 PRINT "ANGLE BETWEEN FIRST PRINCIPAL STRAIN & A ";T1;" DEG"
260 PRINT
270 PRINT "YOUNG'S MODULUS (KN/MM^2) - 0 IF STRESSES NOT REQUIRED";
280 INPUT E
290 IF E=0 THEN 350
300 PRINT "POISSON'S RATIO";
310 INPUT U
320 S1=E/(1-U*U)/1000*(E1+U*E2)
330 S2=E/(1-U*U)/1000*(E2+U*E1)
340 PRINT "PRINCIPAL STRESSES",S1,S2;" N/MM^2"
350 PRINT
360 PRINT "DO YOU WISH TO ANALYSE ANOTHER ROSETTE? INPUT YES OR NO";
370 INPUT Y$
380 IF Y$="YES" THEN 30
390 STOP

READY

RUN

EX6POINT5 22-JUN-81  15:21:25

STRAIN GAUGE ROSETTE ANALYSIS
-----------------------------

INPUT:
STRAINS FOR GAUGES A,B AND C (MICROSTRAIN)? 200,-50,-300
ANGLES (DEG) BETWEEN A & B AND B & C? 60,60
```

```
PRINCIPAL STRAINS              238.675      -338.675   MICROSTRAIN
ANGLE BETWEEN FIRST PRINCIPAL STRAIN & A  15  DEG

YOUNG'S MODULUS (KN/MM^2) - 0 IF STRESSES NOT REQUIRED? 207
POISSON'S RATIO? .29
PRINCIPAL STRESSES             31.7448      -60.8997  N/MM^2

DO YOU WISH TO ANALYSE ANOTHER ROSETTE? INPUT YES OR NO? YES

INPUT:
STRAINS FOR GAUGES A,B AND C (MICROSTRAIN)? 150,430,-310
ANGLES (DEG) BETWEEN A & B AND B & C? 45,45

PRINCIPAL STRAINS              479.464      -639.465   MICROSTRAIN
ANGLE BETWEEN FIRST PRINCIPAL STRAIN & A  32.8628  DEG

YOUNG'S MODULUS (KN/MM^2) - 0 IF STRESSES NOT REQUIRED? 0

DO YOU WISH TO ANALYSE ANOTHER ROSETTE? INPUT YES OR NO? YES

INPUT:
STRAINS FOR GAUGES A,B AND C (MICROSTRAIN)? 150,-310,430
ANGLES (DEG) BETWEEN A & B AND B & C? 270,45

PRINCIPAL STRAINS              479.465      -639.461   MICROSTRAIN
ANGLE BETWEEN FIRST PRINCIPAL STRAIN & A -32.8629  DEG

YOUNG'S MODULUS (KN/MM^2) - 0 IF STRESSES NOT REQUIRED? 0

DO YOU WISH TO ANALYSE ANOTHER ROSETTE? INPUT YES OR NO? NO

STOP AT LINE 390

READY
```

Program notes

(1) The angles between the strain gauges (A1 and B1) are converted to radians in lines 100 and 110. The angle between gauge c and gauge a (namely $\alpha + \beta$) is represented by C1 in line 130.

(2) Equations (6.15) and (6.14) are evaluated in lines 130 to 150 to give T2 representing 2θ.

(3) The sum and difference of the principal strains are determined using Equations (6.16) and (6.17) in lines 160 and 170. The principal strains (E1 and E2) are found from these in lines 190 and 200 using Equations (6.18).

(4) If lines 210 to 230 are omitted, the first principal strain (E1) is not necessarily the highest principal strain – E2 may be instead. This is because the computer always evaluates 2θ (T2) as being less than $90°$ (line 150) whereas it can be $180°$ higher.

(5) The principal stresses are determined from the principal strains in lines 320 and 330 using Equations (6.9). The strains are converted from microstrain and E is converted to units of N/mm^2 for these calculations.

PROBLEMS

(6.1) Write a program to analyse the direct and shear stresses in a bar subject to uniaxial tension. From 'run-time' input of applied tensile stress the program should tabulate the direct and shear stress components on oblique planes at intervals of 5° from 0° to 90° with respect to the longitudinal axis of the bar. Use the results to plot a Mohr's stress circle.

(6.2) The iterative beam design program in Example 6.2 requires the setting of a number of parameters which control the progress of the iteration. As discussed in Program note (6) for that Example, these parameters are given fixed values built into the program.

Analyse the iteration procedure by varying the values of these parameters and printing the values of D at each iteration cycle (C). Hence try to optimise their values.

(6.3) Modify the program in Example 6.1 so that the hollow box beam is designed using the automatic iterative design procedure of Example 6.2.

(6.4) The design of the hollow box section in Example 6.1 neglects possible shear failure of the vertical webs of the section (Figure 6.4).

Alter the program in Example 6.1 so that using 'run-time' input of shear force (in kN) a selected beam section is checked for possible shear failure and modified if necessary. The shear force may either be assumed to be uniformly distributed over the vertical webs or, more accurately, Equation (5.13) can be used to determine the maximum shear stress in the section. It is reasonable to assume that the allowable shear stress is half the allowable direct stress.

(6.5) Example 6.4 describes the analysis of stresses across a beam of rectangular cross-section.

It is instructive to observe how the direction of maximum principal stress changes through the thickness of the beam. Modify the program in Example 6.4 to print the direction of maximum principal stress either instead of one of the stresses, or in addition if TAB printing is used.

(6.6) The program in Example 5.5 when modified according to Problem (5.6) gives direct and shear stress components at any position on the vertical neutral axis of an I-shaped section.

Use the subroutine in Example 6.3 to extend this program to give the principal stresses at any position across the section.

(6.7) Write a program to determine the errors caused by the unobserved misalignment of *one* of the gauges in a strain gauge rosette. Errors in the magnitudes and directions of the principal strains should be calculated for misalignments of up to 5° in either direction with intervals of 1°.

Hint: Modify the program in Example 6.5 so that the main calculations (lines 100 to 230) are performed in a subroutine. Use similar data input to that in Example 6.5 and calculate the principal strains and their orientations, assuming no errors exist. The program should then increase the first angle (α in Figure 6.6) by 5°, recalculate the principal values and then determine the percentage differences (i.e. errors) from the initial solution. This procedure should be repeated for an angle change of 4°, then 3° and so on. The angle α should then be decreased by up to 5°. The results should be presented in tabular form.

(6.8) The general purpose strain gauge rosette program in Example 6.5 could be improved from the point of view of a potential user, if it printed an explanation of its use. In greatest need of explanation is the principle by which clockwise orientation of angles between the gauges gives clockwise positive angles between maximum principal strain and the first gauge (and vice-versa). Modify the program to clarify its use.

(6.9) Simplify the theory in Example 6.5 for the special case of a closed equiangular (60°) strain gauge rosette. Write a program to analyse this type of rosette using 'run-time' input of strains (the angles being built into the program).

(6.10) To analyse the bending of beams of unsymmetrical cross-section, such as L-shaped sections, it is necessary to determine the principal moments of area. These are obtained using equations similar to those for stresses (i.e. Equations (6.2) to (6.5) but with I_{xx} replacing σ_x, I_{yy} replacing σ_y and I_{xy} replacing τ_{xy}).

Study the theory for unsymmetrical bending and principal moments of area in one of the references, page 13, then write a program to determine the principal moments of area for an L-shaped section of arbitrary dimensions.

Chapter 7

Failure

ESSENTIAL THEORY

7.1 Failure concepts

Most structural components are designed to avoid failure. The concept of failure is sometimes limited to mean only material fracture but in a wider sense any inability of a component to perform its function can be termed failure.

In one of its senses failure may occur when the material first yields. The prediction of yielding under complex states of stress requires the use of so-called *yield criteria*. A complication in the prediction of first yield is the possible presence of *stress concentrations*. Around a geometric discontinuity, such as a corner or hole, there are localised stresses which are much higher than the nominal stresses in that region. The degree of stress concentration is measured by a *stress concentration factor K_t* where

$$K_t = \frac{\text{actual peak stress}}{\text{nominal stress}} \tag{7.1}$$

Values of K_t have been determined for various geometries (see references, page 13).

The existence of stress concentrations can lead to premature failure of brittle materials but under static loading, ductile materials have the ability upon first yield to transfer the load to regions of lower stress. However crack-like defects can cause a premature and *brittle fracture* of even ductile materials particularly in thick components. If the loading is of a cyclic nature any stress concentration can initiate a crack. Such a crack propagates slowly under cyclic loading until fracture eventually occurs (*fatigue failure*). Brittle fracture and fatigue failure can be analysed using *fracture mechanics,* an approach based on the assumption of cracks being present in a material.

Excessive deformation can represent a practical criterion for failure. Metals at high temperatures and non-metals such as plastics, timber and concrete at ambient temperatures can *creep*. Creep is a gradual increase in deformation at a constant load and associated with this behaviour is a gradual decrease in stress (*stress relaxation*) when the deformation is held constant.

A most important form of deformation-limited failure is the instability condition called *buckling* whereby components in compression suffer large lateral deformations at stresses below those necessary to cause yield or fracture.

7.2 Yield criteria

A number of theories have been developed which relate the principal stresses at a point in a material (σ_1, σ_2, σ_3) to the yield strength of the material in simple tension (σ_Y). Their object is to predict when yielding will first occur under complex stress conditions. The theories have been largely discredited if they do not acknowledge that yielding is associated with shear actions and does not occur under hydrostatic loading (however large). There are two criteria which fulfil these conditions. They both assume that the yield strength in compression equals that in tension.

(1) *Maximum shear stress criterion (Tresca)*
This criterion is usually named after Tresca. With the convention $\sigma_1 > \sigma_2 > \sigma_3$ the maximum shear stress at a point is $\frac{1}{2}(\sigma_1 - \sigma_3)$ (see Section 6.5).

Tresca's criterion proposes that yielding first occurs when the maximum shear stress in the complex stress system equals the maximum shear stress in uniaxial tension (yield strength σ_Y). In simple tension $\sigma_1 = \sigma_Y$, $\sigma_2 = 0$, $\sigma_3 = 0$ and the maximum shear stress is $\sigma_Y/2$.

The maximum shear stress criterion predicts, therefore, that yielding just occurs when

$$\sigma_1 - \sigma_3 = \sigma_Y \tag{7.2}$$

(2) *Maximum shear strain energy criterion (Von Mises)*
This criterion is usually named after Von Mises (it is also associated with Huber and Hencky). Distortion (as opposed to volume change) of an element of material is caused by the principal stress differences (shear stress). The strain energy per unit volume (U_s) associated with this distortion or shear is given by

$$U_s = \frac{1}{12G} \left[(\sigma_1 - \sigma_2)^2 + (\sigma_2 - \sigma_3)^2 + (\sigma_3 - \sigma_1)^2 \right] \tag{7.3}$$

Von Mises' criterion proposes that yielding first occurs when the maximum shear strain energy in the complex stress system equals that in uniaxial tension. In simple tension $\sigma_1 = \sigma_Y$, $\sigma_2 = 0$, $\sigma_3 = 0$ and the shear strain energy is $2\sigma_Y^2/12G$.

The maximum shear strain energy criterion predicts that yielding first occurs when

$$(\sigma_1 - \sigma_2)^2 + (\sigma_2 - \sigma_3)^2 + (\sigma_3 - \sigma_1)^2 = 2\sigma_Y^2 \qquad (7.4)$$

Both of these yield criteria are widely used. Von Mises' criterion is well supported by experimental evidence, Tresca's criterion is somewhat conservative but it is particularly easy to use.

7.3 Brittle fracture

The failure of a brittle material under complex stress conditions (with principal stresses σ_1, σ_2 and σ_3) can be related to the uniaxial tensile strength (σ_F).

One criterion predicts failure when the maximum principal stress in the complex stress system equals the maximum principal stress in simple tension, i.e. failure occurs when

$$\sigma_1 = \sigma_F \qquad (7.5)$$

The theory can be made to apply to different strengths in tension and compression − most brittle materials have a higher compressive strength.

The unexpected brittle fracture of more ductile materials under some circumstances is more difficult to predict. Historically, the approach has been based on impact testing and the determination of transition temperatures between ductile and brittle behaviour. Latterly, the more rational fracture mechanics approach has been used.

7.4 Fracture mechanics

Fracture mechanics acknowledges the existence of cracks in a material and predicts the critical crack length for brittle fracture to occur. In its simplest form, fracture mechanics holds for linear elastic materials with only local yielding at the crack tip. It can be extended to a wide range of materials and circumstances.

Fracture mechanics is based on a consideration of the energy requirements for crack growth. Strain energy is released from the region unloaded by the presence of a crack. Energy is required to break atomic bonds at the crack tip in order for a crack to grow. For a short crack length or low applied stress level the released energy is insufficient to fuel crack growth. If the crack is of sufficient (critical) length or the

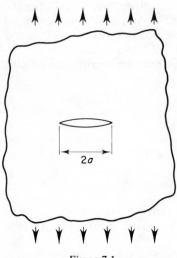

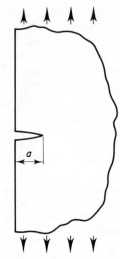

Figure 7.1   Figure 7.2

applied stress is high enough, the released energy causes the crack to grow rapidly and catastrophically without any increase in applied stress.

Figures 7.1 and 7.2 show regions of very large sheets with, respectively, a sharp internal crack length $2a$ and a sharp edge crack length a. If these sheets are subjected to applied tensile loading (stress σ), the theory of fracture mechanics shows that

$$K_I = Q\sigma\sqrt{(\pi a)} \qquad (7.6)$$

where K_I is called the *stress intensity factor* and Q is a dimensionless constant which depends on the geometry of the cracked configuration. Q equals 1 for the case shown in Figure 7.1, and 1.12 for that shown in Figure 7.2. Values of Q are available for a wide range of geometries.

If the applied stress level reaches a critical level (σ_c) the crack propagates catastrophically as discussed above. This occurs when

$$K_{IC} = Q\sigma_c\sqrt{(\pi a)} \qquad (7.7)$$

where K_{IC} is known as the *critical stress intensity factor* or *fracture toughness* of the material. K_{IC} is a measure of the resistance of a material to brittle fracture and, like Young's modulus, it is a material constant (though it varies with temperature, etc.). It is usually expressed in units of $MNm^{-3/2}$.

For a material of known fracture toughness, Equation (7.7) can be used to predict the critical stress level for a known configuration (Q) with a known* crack length (a or $2a$).

*Measured by non-destructive testing techniques (NDT) such as penetrants, X-rays, ultrasonics and eddy currents.

Alternatively the equation can be written as

$$K_{IC} = Q\sigma\sqrt{(\pi a_c)} \qquad (7.8)$$

In this form the critical crack length (a_c or $2a_c$) can be predicted for a known loading. If a crack of this (or greater length) is present there will be catastrophic failure when the stated load is reached.

The fracture mechanics approach is fully described in reference 7, page 13.

7.5 Fatigue

Cyclic loading causes fatigue failure at stresses below a material's static strength. Fatigue cracks initiate at points of stress concentration and propagate during cyclic loading until they reach a critical length, when catastrophic brittle fracture occurs.

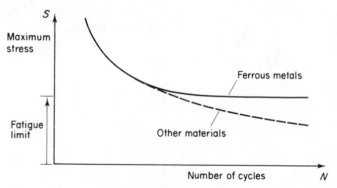

Figure 7.3

The classical portrayal of fatigue data is the S–N curve (Figure 7.3). This shows the number of cycles to failure (N) of a specimen subjected to alternating tensile and compressive loading (maximum stress S). A number of component design procedures are based on the use of S–N curves.

Fracture mechanics can be used to predict the rate of fatigue crack propagation. For cyclic loading between a minimum stress σ_{min} and a maximum stress σ_{max}, Equation (7.6) can be used to determine the range of stress intensity factor ΔK, i.e.

$$\Delta K = Q(\sigma_{max} - \sigma_{min})\sqrt{(\pi a)} \qquad (7.9)$$

The rate of crack growth per cycle of loading (da/dN) can be predicted from the Paris law

$$\frac{da}{dN} = C(\Delta K)^m \qquad (7.10)$$

where C and m are empirical constants. Integration of this equation gives the number of cycles (N_1) for a crack to grow from an initial length a_0 to a length a_1. Thus

$$N_1 = \int_{a_0}^{a_1} \frac{\mathrm{d}a}{C(\Delta K)^m} \tag{7.11}$$

where a_1 cannot exceed the critical crack length for brittle fracture. For some problems this integral can be evaluated simply, but if Q is a function of crack length numerical techniques must be used.

It is possible to predict the number of loading cycles (life) before a critical length is reached or to define inspection intervals for monitoring sub-critical crack growth.

7.6 Buckling

When a long member (a *column* or *strut*) is compressed axially it buckles laterally instead of failing in direct compression.

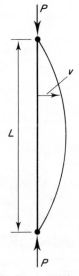

Figure 7.4

The simplest theoretical analysis is for a column, length L, which is pinned at its ends and subjected to a compressive axial load P (Figure 7.4). Application of Equation (5.15) gives

$$EI \frac{\mathrm{d}^2 v}{\mathrm{d}x^2} = Pv \tag{7.12}$$

The solution of this equation shows that as P increases the lateral deflection (v) is zero until P reaches a critical value (P_E) when large deflections occur (Figure 7.5). In practice, eccentricity of loading or initial curvature of the member are difficult to avoid and the column starts to deflect at low loads.

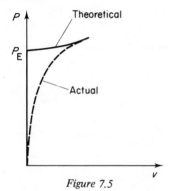

Figure 7.5

The value of the critical load P_E (known as the *Euler buckling load*) is given by

$$P_E = \frac{\pi^2 EI}{L^2} \qquad (7.13)$$

It is important to note that the second moment of area (I) is the *least* value for the cross-section.

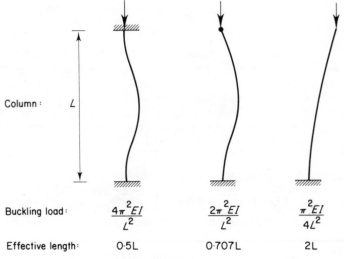

Column :	L		
Buckling load :	$\dfrac{4\pi^2 EI}{L^2}$	$\dfrac{2\pi^2 EI}{L^2}$	$\dfrac{\pi^2 EI}{4L^2}$
Effective length :	0·5L	0·707L	2L

Figure 7.6

As shown in Figure 7.6, similar buckling load expressions, but with different numeric coefficients, are found for columns with other end conditions. Equation (7.13) is often used for all cases with the column length modified to be an *effective length* of a pinned column (Figure 7.6).

Equation (7.13) can be written in terms of the direct stress (σ_E) for a column with the cross-sectional area A. Thus

$$\sigma_E = \frac{P_E}{A} = \frac{\pi^2 E}{(L/r)^2} \tag{7.14}$$

where r is the minimum radius of gyration for the cross-section as defined by Equation (5.11). The term L/r defines a *slenderness ratio*.

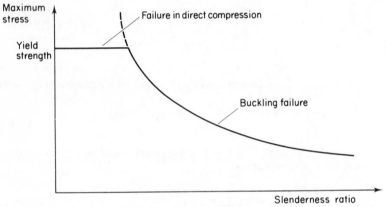

Figure 7.7

As shown in Figure 7.7, resistance to buckling increases rapidly for short column lengths. If very short, the column fails in direct compression (at its yield strength for a ductile material).

Empirical buckling formulae are often used, particularly to cope with the transition region between buckling and direct compressive failure. The empirical formulae used in design codes have built-in safety factors.

WORKED EXAMPLES

Example 7.1 Safety factors using yield criteria

Write a program to determine safety factors assuming yielding is governed by

    (1) the maximum shear stress criterion (Tresca), or
    (2) the maximum shear strain energy criterion (Von Mises).

Example 7.1 Safety factors using yield criteria   105

Values of the principal stresses σ_1, σ_2 and σ_3 and the material yield strength should be specified by 'run-time' input.

Use the program to investigate a number of states of stress.

```
EX7POINT1 30-JUN-81  09:57:00

10 PRINT "SAFETY FACTORS USING TRESCA AND VON MISES YIELD CRITERIA"
20 PRINT "--------------------------------------------------------"
30 PRINT
40 PRINT "INPUT (USING CONSISTENT UNITS):"
50 PRINT "YIELD STRESS (0 TO STOP)";
60 INPUT Y
70 IF Y>0 THEN 90
80 STOP
90 PRINT "PRINCIPAL STRESSES SIG1,SIG2,SIG3";
100 INPUT S1,S2,S3
110 F1=Y/(S1-S3)
120 PRINT "TRESCA SAFETY FACTOR";F1
130 F2=(S1-S2)^2+(S2-S3)^2+(S3-S1)^2
140 F2=Y*SQR(2/F2)
150 PRINT "VON MISES SAFETY FACTOR";F2
160 GO TO 30

READY


RUN


EX7POINT1 30-JUN-81   09:57:32

SAFETY FACTORS USING TRESCA AND VON MISES YIELD CRITERIA
--------------------------------------------------------

INPUT (USING CONSISTENT UNITS):
YIELD STRESS (0 TO STOP)? 250
PRINCIPAL STRESSES SIG1,SIG2,SIG3? 100,50,0
TRESCA SAFETY FACTOR 2.5
VON MISES SAFETY FACTOR 2.88675

INPUT (USING CONSISTENT UNITS):
YIELD STRESS (0 TO STOP)? 250
PRINCIPAL STRESSES SIG1,SIG2,SIG3? 100,0,-50
TRESCA SAFETY FACTOR 1.66667
VON MISES SAFETY FACTOR 1.88982

INPUT (USING CONSISTENT UNITS):
YIELD STRESS (0 TO STOP)? 0

STOP AT LINE 80

READY
```

Program notes

(1) The safety factor using the maximum shear stress (Tresca) criterion is determined as F1 in lines 110 using Equation (7.2). The safety factor using the maximum shear strain energy (Von Mises) criterion is determined as F2 in lines 130 and 140 using Equation (7.4).

(2) Note that the Tresca criterion is more conservative than the Von Mises criterion. In order to investigate a full range of different stress states, the program could be modified so that it automatically generates a range of values of σ_1, σ_2 and σ_3.

Example 7.2 Circular shaft design

Write a program to design (i.e. determine the diameter of) a solid circular shaft to resist a prescribed torque and bending moment. In addition to specifying the torque (in kNm) and bending moment (in kNm) the program should use 'run-time' input of the material yield strength (in N/mm^2) and a safety factor with which to obtain a maximum allowable stress for design purposes.

The program should determine the necessary shaft diameter (in mm) using both the Tresca and Von Mises yield criteria. Design a shaft to resist a maximum torque of 25 kNm and a maximum bending moment of 15 kNm using a safety factor of 2 for a material with a yield strength of 250 N/mm^2.

```
EX7POINT2  30-JUN-81   10:00:12

10 PRINT "DESIGN OF SOLID CIRCULAR SHAFTS SUBJECT TO BENDING AND TORSION"
20 PRINT "-----------------------------------------------------------------"
30 PRINT
40 PRINT "INPUT:"
50 PRINT "MATERIAL YIELD STRENGTH (N/MM^2) - 0 TO STOP";
60 INPUT Y
70 IF Y>0 THEN 90
80 STOP
90 PRINT "SAFETY FACTOR";
100 INPUT F
110 PRINT "MAXIMUM TORQUE (KNM)";
120 INPUT T
130 T=T*1.00000E+06
140 PRINT "MAXIMUM BENDING MOMENT (KNM)";
150 INPUT M
160 M=M*1.00000E+06
170 X9=32*M/3.14159
180 Y9=0
190 T9=16*T/3.14159
200 GOSUB 1000
210 GOSUB 2000
220 D3=(S1-S3)/(Y/F)
230 PRINT "TRESCA YIELD CRITERION: SHAFT DIAMETER";D3^(1/3);"MM"
240 D6=((S1-S2)^2+(S2-S3)^2+(S3-S1)^2)/(2*(Y/F)^2)
250 PRINT "VON MISES YIELD CRITERION: SHAFT DIAMETER";D6^(1/6);"MM"
260 GO TO 30
1000 REM SUBROUTINE TO DETERMINE PRINCIPAL STRESSES (P1 AND P2) AND
1010 REM ANGLE AO FROM SIGX (X9), SIGY (Y9) AND TAUXY (T9)
1020 P1=(Y9+X9)/2+SQR(((Y9-X9)/2)^2+T9*T9)
1030 P2=(Y9+X9)/2-SQR(((Y9-X9)/2)^2+T9*T9)
1040 IF Y9=X9 THEN 1080
1050 AO=ATN(-2*T9/(Y9-X9))/2
1060 AO=AO*180/3.14159
1070 GO TO 1090
1080 AO=0
1090 RETURN
2000 REM SUBROUTINE TO SORT 2D PRINCIPAL STRESSES (P1,P2)
2010 REM INTO 3D PRINCIPAL STRESSES (S1,S2,S3)
2020 IF P1>0 THEN 2070
2030 S1=0
2040 S2=P1
2050 S3=P2
2060 GO TO 2140
2070 S1=P1
2080 IF P2<0 THEN 2120
2090 S2=P2
```

Example 7.2 Circular shaft design   107

```
2100  S3=0
2110  GO TO 2140
2120  S2=0
2130  S3=P2
2140  RETURN
```

READY

RUN

EX7POINT2 30-JUN-81   10:01:10

DESIGN OF SOLID CIRCULAR SHAFTS SUBJECT TO BENDING AND TORSION

```
INPUT:
MATERIAL YIELD STRENGTH (N/MM^2) - 0 TO STOP? 250
SAFETY FACTOR? 2
MAXIMUM TORQUE (KNM)? 25
MAXIMUM BENDING MOMENT (KNM)? 15
TRESCA YIELD CRITERION: SHAFT DIAMETER 133.434 MM
VON MISES YIELD CRITERION: SHAFT DIAMETER 128.992 MM

INPUT:
MATERIAL YIELD STRENGTH (N/MM^2) - 0 TO STOP? 0

STOP AT LINE 80
```

READY

Program notes

(1) The yield criteria must be applied at the point(s) in the shaft where the stresses give the highest values according to the criteria. This is clearly on the outside of the shaft where the direct stress due to the bending moment and the stress due to the torque are both maximum.

From Equations (5.8) and (5.12) with y_{max} equal to $D/2$ the maximum direct stress

$$\sigma_x = \frac{32M}{\pi d^3} \tag{7.15}$$

Similarly, from Equation (4.15) with r_{max} equal to $D/2$ the maximum shear stress

$$\tau_{xy} = \frac{16T}{\pi d^3} \tag{7.16}$$

For design purposes the unknown 'd^3' terms are omitted from these expressions which are then represented by X9 and T9 respectively in lines 170 and 190. The other direct stress component σ_y is zero at all points in the shaft (Y9 in line 180).

(2) The subroutine from Example 6.3 is used to determine the principal stresses (lines 1000–1090). This gives the two-dimensional principal stresses P1 and P2 without the missing d^3 terms.

(3) To use the yield criteria correctly it is necessary to determine the three-dimensional principal stresses in the correct order, i.e. $\sigma_1 > \sigma_2 > \sigma_3$. For this problem the principal stresses are represented by P1, P2 and zero (normal to the surface of the shaft). Another subroutine, in lines 2000–2140, is used to sort the 2D principal stresses (P1, P2 and zero) into the 3D principal stresses (S1, S2 and S3).

(4) These principal stress values (without the missing d^3 terms) are substituted into the yield criteria to determine the required shaft diameters.

For example, using Equation (7.2) for the Tresca criterion

$$d^3 = \frac{\sigma_1 - \sigma_3}{\sigma_Y/F} \tag{7.17}$$

where the values of σ_1 and σ_3 (i.e. S1 and S3) are computed without the unknown d^3 terms as described above. F is the safety factor.

The diameter according to the Tresca (maximum shear stress) criterion is determined in lines 220 to 230. The diameter according to the Von Mises (maximum shear strain energy) criterion is determined in lines 240 to 250 using Equation (7.4).

Example 7.3 Fracture mechanics parameters

Write a program to evaluate the fracture mechanics equation

$$K_{IC} = Q\sigma_c\sqrt{(\pi a)}$$

if any three of the four parameters are specified.

```
EX7POINT3   1-JUL-81   09:41:18

10 PRINT "CALCULATION OF FRACTURE MECHANICS PARAMETERS"
20 PRINT "-----------------------------------------------"
30 PRINT
40 PRINT "**USE CONSISTENT UNITS & INPUT 0 FOR UNKNOWN PARAMETER**"
50 PRINT
60 PRINT "INPUT:"
70 PRINT "GEOMETRIC CONSTANT Q";
80 INPUT Q
90 PRINT "CRACK LENGTH OR HALF LENGTH A";
100 INPUT A
110 PRINT "REMOTE STRESS TO CAUSE FAST FRACTURE S";
120 INPUT S
130 PRINT "FRACTURE TOUGHNESS K";
140 INPUT K
150 PRINT
160 IF Q=0 THEN 220
170 IF A=0 THEN 250
180 IF S=0 THEN 280
190 IF K=0 THEN 310
200 PRINT "YOU HAVE SPECIFIED ALL FOUR PARAMETERS!"
210 GO TO 50
220 Q=K/(S*SQR(3.14159*A))
230 PRINT "GEOMETRIC FACTOR Q = ";Q
240 GO TO 330
```

Example 7.3 Fracture mechanics parameters 109

```
250 A=(K/(Q*S))^2/3.14159
260 PRINT "CRACK LENGTH OR HALF LENGTH A = ";A
270 GO TO 330
280 S=K/(Q*SQR(3.14159*A))
290 PRINT "REMOTE STRESS TO CAUSE FAST FRACTURE S = ";S
300 GO TO 330
310 K=Q*S*SQR(3.14159*A)
320 PRINT "FRACTURE TOUGHNESS K = ";K
330 PRINT
340 PRINT "INPUT YES IF YOU WISH TO DO ANOTHER CALCULATION";
350 INPUT Y$
360 IF Y$="YES" THEN 30
370 STOP

READY

RUN

EX7POINT3  1-JUL-81  09:42:08

CALCULATION OF FRACTURE MECHANICS PARAMETERS
--------------------------------------------

**USE CONSISTENT UNITS & INPUT 0 FOR UNKNOWN PARAMETER**

INPUT:
GEOMETRIC CONSTANT Q? 1.12
CRACK LENGTH OR HALF LENGTH A? .007
REMOTE STRESS TO CAUSE FAST FRACTURE S? 330
FRACTURE TOUGHNESS K? 55

YOU HAVE SPECIFIED ALL FOUR PARAMETERS!

INPUT:
GEOMETRIC CONSTANT Q? 1.12
CRACK LENGTH OR HALF LENGTH A? .007
REMOTE STRESS TO CAUSE FAST FRACTURE S? 330
FRACTURE TOUGHNESS K? 0

FRACTURE TOUGHNESS K =  54.8095

INPUT YES IF YOU WISH TO DO ANOTHER CALCULATION? YES

**USE CONSISTENT UNITS & INPUT 0 FOR UNKNOWN PARAMETER**

INPUT:
GEOMETRIC CONSTANT Q? 1.12
CRACK LENGTH OR HALF LENGTH A? .005
REMOTE STRESS TO CAUSE FAST FRACTURE S? 0
FRACTURE TOUGHNESS K? 54.81

REMOTE STRESS TO CAUSE FAST FRACTURE S =  390.465

INPUT YES IF YOU WISH TO DO ANOTHER CALCULATION? NO

STOP AT LINE 370

READY
```

Program notes

(1) The program uses a zero value to indicate the unknown parameter
and hence to determine the form of equation to be evaluated (lines
160– 190). The program checks that all four parameters have not been
specified (line 200) but it does contain a logical flaw (see Program note
(2), Example 4.3).

(2) The problem as specified requires the evaluation of Equation (7.7) in which the applied stress has a critical value. The program is equally valid for Equation (7.8), in which the crack length is critical, or for Equation (7.6). The latter equation can be used to determine the stress intensity factors for sub-critical values of crack length and applied stress. The degree by which the stress intensity factor is less than the critical stress intensity factor (fracture toughness) gives an indication of the nearness to catastrophic brittle fracture.

(3) The program assumes the use of consistent units and prints a warning to that effect (line 40). The program could be modified to use specific units, for instance crack length in mm.

Example 7.4 Cumulative fatigue damage

A method called *Miner's Rule* can be used to predict when fatigue failure will occur after a number of alternating stress loadings have taken place, each for an insufficient number of cycles to cause failure separately.

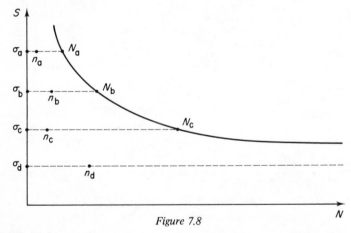

Figure 7.8

Suppose stresses σ_a, σ_b, σ_c, . . . individually cause fatigue failure after N_a, N_b, N_c, . . . cycles respectively as shown in Figure 7.8. Suppose further that these stresses are applied for n_a, n_b, n_c, . . . cycles respectively — individually they do not cause fatigue failure.

According to Miner's rule, fatigue failure occurs when

$$n_a/N_a + n_b/N_b + n_c/N_c + \ldots = 1 \text{ or } \Sigma \frac{n}{N} = 1 \qquad (7.18)$$

This is not an exact theory and in practice $0.6 < \Sigma \dfrac{n}{N} < 1.5$

Example 7.4 Cumulative fatigue damage 111

Note: a stress level below the fatigue limit (σ_d in Figure 7.8) causes no damage ($N_d \to \infty \therefore n_d/N_d = 0$).

Using Miner's rule for a material with a fatigue limit, write a program to analyse cumulative fatigue damage as follows

(1) note that it is common to assume that the fatigue strength reduces linearly with number of loading cycles when plotted on a logarithmic basis as shown in Figure 7.9,

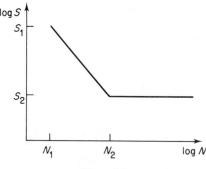

Figure 7.9

(2) use READ and DATA statements to specify the $S-N$ data for a material in terms of its fatigue strength (S1) at the lowest number of cycles for which data are available (N1) and its fatigue limit (strength S2 at N2 cycles). The notation is shown in Figure 7.9,

(3) use READ and DATA statements to specify each stress level S (σ_a, etc. in Figure 7.7) and number of loading cycles C (n_a, etc. in Figure 7.7) for any particular cumulative damage problem. This enables a complete load spectrum to be specified,

(4) at each stress level S use logarithmic interpolation to determine the endurance N (N_a, etc. in Figure 7.8),

(5) tabulate the damage fraction C/N for each stress level and add them to give the total damage caused by the specified load spectrum and the number of times the load spectrum can be endured.

```
EX7POINT4   1-JUL-81   09:46:12

1 DATA "MILD STEEL",360,1E4,180,1E6
10 DATA 300,1E4,280,1E3,260,2E3,250,2E4,220,5E3,200,5E4,180,1E4,160,1E6,0
11 DATA 400,1E5,250,1E7,-1
100 PRINT "CUMULATIVE FATIGUE DAMAGE USING MINER'S RULE"
110 PRINT "-----------------------------------------------------"
120 PRINT
130 PRINT "S-N DATA FOR ";
140 READ A$,S1,N1,S2,N2
150 PRINT A$
160 PRINT "FATIGUE STRENGTH";S1;"N/MM^2 AT";N1;"CYCLES"
170 PRINT "REDUCING TO";S2;"N/MM^2 (FATIGUE LIMIT) AT";N2;"CYCLES"
180 PRINT
```

```
190 PRINT "CUMULATIVE DAMAGE ANALYSIS:"
200 PRINT
210 PRINT "STRESS","NUMBER OF","ENDURANCE AT","DAMAGE"
220 PRINT "(N/MM^2)","LOAD CYCLES","THIS STRESS","FRACTION"
230 D=0
240 READ S
250 IF S>0 THEN 310
260 PRINT " "," "," ","-----------------"
270 PRINT " "," ","TOTAL",D
280 PRINT
290 PRINT "THIS LOAD SPECTRUM CAN BE ENDURED APPROXIMATELY";1/D;"TIMES"
300 STOP
310 READ C
320 IF S<=S1 THEN 350
330 PRINT S;"EXCEEDS MAXIMUM VALUE";S1;"N/MM^2 FOR WHICH DATA AVAILABLE"
340 STOP
350 IF S<=S2 THEN 390
360 N=LOG(N2)-(LOG(N2)-LOG(N1))*(LOG(S)-LOG(S2))/(LOG(S1)-LOG(S2))
370 N=EXP(N)
380 GO TO 400
390 N=1.00000E+30
400 D=D+C/N
410 PRINT S,C,N,C/N
420 GO TO 240

READY


RUN


EX7POINT4  1-JUL-81  09:47:02

CUMULATIVE FATIGUE DAMAGE USING MINER'S RULE
----------------------------------------------------

S-N DATA FOR MILD STEEL
FATIGUE STRENGTH 360 N/MM^2 AT 10000 CYCLES
REDUCING TO 180 N/MM^2 (FATIGUE LIMIT) AT 1.00000E+06 CYCLES

CUMULATIVE DAMAGE ANALYSIS:
```

STRESS (N/MM^2)	NUMBER OF LOAD CYCLES	ENDURANCE AT THIS STRESS	DAMAGE FRACTION
300	10000	33579.1	.297804
280	1000	53105.7	.0188304
260	2000	86890.1	.0230176
250	20000	112755	.177375
220	5000	263625	.0189663
200	50000	496586	.100688
180	10000	1.00000E+30	1.00000E-26
160	1.00000E+06	1.00000E+30	1.00000E-24
		TOTAL	.636681

```
THIS LOAD SPECTRUM CAN BE ENDURED APPROXIMATELY 1.57064 TIMES

STOP AT LINE 300

READY
```

Program notes

(1) The program follows the procedure outlined above. The program interprets a zero or negative value of S (read in line 240) as signifying that the data are complete (line 250).

(2) The variable D represents the total fractional damage caused by the

Example 7.5 Buckling calculations   113

specified load spectrum. It is initially set to zero (line 230). The individual damage fractions are then added to D in line 400.

(3) The logarithmic interpolation is done in lines 360 and 370 to give the endurance (N) for each stress level (S). A warning is printed (line 330) and the program stops if S is higher than the maximum available fatigue strength (S1). No damage is caused by stress levels that are lower than the fatigue limit (S2) so no interpolation is then necessary (line 350).

Example 7.5 Buckling calculations

Write a program to determine

(1) the minimum slenderness ratio of a column for which Euler buckling applies — specify the Young's modulus of the material and its maximum compressive stress,

(2) the minimum column length for which Euler buckling applies using the material specified above and one of the following cross-sections: solid circular, hollow circular, square solid,

(3) the slenderness ratio and load capacity for a column of specified length and cross-section and material defined above.

```
EX7POINT5  1-JUL-81  09:50:07

10 PRINT "EULER BUCKLING CALCULATIONS"
20 PRINT "--------------------------------"
30 PRINT
40 PRINT "INPUT:"
50 PRINT "ELASTIC MODULUS E (KN/MM^2)";
60 INPUT E
70 E=E*1000
80 PRINT "MAX COMPRESSIVE STRESS <= PROPORTIONAL LIMIT (N/MM^2)";
90 INPUT S
100 L1=3.14159*SQR(E/S)
110 PRINT
120 PRINT "MIN SLENDERNESS RATIO FOR EULER BUCKLING";L1
130 PRINT
140 PRINT "CALCULATIONS FOR SPECIFIC COLUMN CROSS-SECTION:"
150 PRINT "INPUT 0( TO STOP),1(SOLID CIRCULAR), 2(HOLLOW CIRCULAR)"
160 PRINT "3(SOLID SQUARE)";
170 INPUT Z
180 ON Z+1 GOSUB 1000,2000,3000,4000
190 R=SQR(I/A)
200 PRINT "CROSS-SECTION AREA";A;"MM^2"
210 PRINT "SECOND MOMENT OF AREA";I;"MM^4"
220 PRINT "RADIUS OF GYRATION";R;"MM"
230 PRINT
240 PRINT "MIN COLUMN LENGTH FOR EULER BUCKLING";L1*R/1000;"M"
250 PRINT
260 PRINT "INPUT 'EFFECTIVE' LENGTH OF ACTUAL COLUMN (M) - 0 TO STOP";
270 INPUT L
280 PRINT
290 IF L>0 THEN 300
295 STOP
300 PRINT "SLENDERNESS RATIO";L*1000/R
310 IF L>L1*R/1000 THEN 360
320 PRINT "EULER BUCKLING FORMULA NOT APPLICABLE"
330 PRINT "MAX LOAD CAPACITY NOT GREATER THAN";S*A/1000;"KN"
```

```
340 PRINT "IT MAY BE DESIRABLE TO USE AN EMPIRICAL FORMULA"
350 GO TO 130
360 P=3.14159^2*E*I/(L*L*1.00000E+06)
370 PRINT "MAX LOAD BEFORE EULER BUCKLING";P/1000;"KN"
380 GO TO 130
1000 REM STOP SUBROUTINE
1010 STOP
1020 RETURN
2000 REM SOLID CIRCULAR COLUMN SUBROUTINE
2010 PRINT
2020 PRINT "INPUT DIAMETER (MM)";
2030 INPUT D
2040 A=3.14159*D*D/4
2050 I=3.14159*D^4/64
2060 RETURN
3000 REM HOLLOW CIRCULAR COLUMN SUBROUTINE
3010 PRINT
3020 PRINT "INPUT DIAMETERS (MM): EXTERNAL,INTERNAL";
3030 INPUT D2,D1
3040 A=3.14159*(D2*D2-D1*D1)/4
3050 I=3.14159*(D2^4-D1^4)/64
3060 RETURN
4000 REM SOLID SQUARE COLUMN SUBROUTINE
4010 PRINT
4020 PRINT "INPUT SIDE LENGTH (MM)";
4030 INPUT D
4040 A=D*D
4050 I=D^4/12
4060 RETURN

READY


RUN


EX7POINT5  1-JUL-81   09:51:32

EULER BUCKLING CALCULATIONS
---------------------------

INPUT:
ELASTIC MODULUS E (KN/MM^2)? 207
MAX COMPRESSIVE STRESS <= PROPORTIONAL LIMIT (N/MM^2)? 200

MIN SLENDERNESS RATIO FOR EULER BUCKLING 101.069

CALCULATIONS FOR SPECIFIC COLUMN CROSS-SECTION:
INPUT 0( TO STOP),1(SOLID CIRCULAR), 2(HOLLOW CIRCULAR)
3(SOLID SQUARE)? 1

INPUT DIAMETER (MM)? 20
CROSS-SECTION AREA 314.159 MM^2
SECOND MOMENT OF AREA 7853.97 MM^4
RADIUS OF GYRATION 5 MM

MIN COLUMN LENGTH FOR EULER BUCKLING .505347 M

INPUT 'EFFECTIVE' LENGTH OF ACTUAL COLUMN (M) - 0 TO STOP? 1

SLENDERNESS RATIO 200
MAX LOAD BEFORE EULER BUCKLING 16.0457 KN

CALCULATIONS FOR SPECIFIC COLUMN CROSS-SECTION:
INPUT 0( TO STOP),1(SOLID CIRCULAR), 2(HOLLOW CIRCULAR)
3(SOLID SQUARE)? 2

INPUT DIAMETERS (MM): EXTERNAL,INTERNAL? 25,20
CROSS-SECTION AREA 176.714 MM^2
SECOND MOMENT OF AREA 11320.8 MM^4
RADIUS OF GYRATION 8.00391 MM
```

Example 7.6 Fracture toughness test   115

```
MIN COLUMN LENGTH FOR EULER BUCKLING .80895 M

INPUT 'EFFECTIVE' LENGTH OF ACTUAL COLUMN (M) - 0 TO STOP? 1

SLENDERNESS RATIO 124.939
MAX LOAD BEFORE EULER BUCKLING 23.1284 KN

CALCULATIONS FOR SPECIFIC COLUMN CROSS-SECTION:
INPUT 0( TO STOP),1(SOLID CIRCULAR), 2(HOLLOW CIRCULAR)
3(SOLID SQUARE)? 0

STOP AT LINE 1010

READY
```

Program notes

(1) The minimum slenderness ratio L1 is determined in line 100 using Equation (7.14).

(2) A computed GOSUB statement is used in line 180 to find the subroutine for the chosen cross-section. Each subroutine determines the cross-section area (A) and second moment of area (I).

(3) Line 360 used Equation (7.13) to determine the Euler buckling load (P). For end conditions other than pinned, the column length (L) in line 270 should represent the effective length as discussed in Section 7.6. Figure 7.7 shows the behaviour represented by the calculations in this program.

Example 7.6 Fracture toughness test

Effective use of the fracture mechanics approach requires the accurate experimental determination of fracture toughness (K_{IC}). Care must be

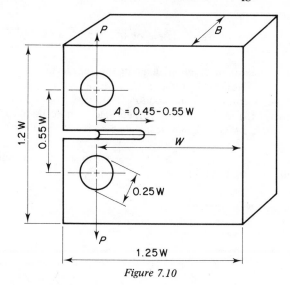

Figure 7.10

taken to ensure that any particular test is valid and, in particular, the amount of plastic deformation must be small.

One such test uses the compact tension specimen shown in Figure 7.10. The machined specimen is subjected to cyclic loading to produce a short, sharp, fatigue crack. A static test is then performed to produce brittle fracture of the specimen at a failure load P_Q.

The fracture toughness is calculated using the equation

$$K_{IC} = \frac{P_Q}{BW^{1/2}} \left[29.6 \left(\frac{a}{W}\right)^{1/2} - 185.5 \left(\frac{a}{W}\right)^{3/2} + 655.7 \left(\frac{a}{W}\right)^{5/2} \right.$$

$$\left. -1017 \left(\frac{a}{W}\right)^{7/2} + 638.9 \left(\frac{a}{W}\right)^{9/2} \right] \qquad (7.19)$$

where the dimensions are measured in metres.

The test is valid if

(1) the zone of plastic deformation around the crack tip is small. The size of this plastic zone is a function of fracture toughness (K_{IC}) and yield strength (σ_Y) and the test is valid if

$$\text{the crack length} \quad a \geqslant 2.5 \left(\frac{K_{IC}}{\sigma_Y}\right)^2$$

$$\text{the thickness} \quad B \geqslant 2.5 \left(\frac{K_{IC}}{\sigma_Y}\right)^2 \qquad (7.20)$$

$$\text{the width dimension} \, W \geqslant 5 \left(\frac{K_{IC}}{\sigma_Y}\right)^2$$

(2) The maximum recorded load in the tensile test is not greater than $1.1P_Q$. During this test a plot is made of load against the distance the crack opens. The failure load P_Q is obtained from a 5% offset to this curve. If the maximum recorded load is more than 10% higher than P_Q it is a sign that significant yielding has taken place.

Write a program to monitor this test procedure, determine K_{IC} and do the necessary validity checks.

```
EX7POINT6 12-MAY-82  12:48:09

10 PRINT "FRACTURE TOUGHNESS TEST: COMPACT TENSION SPECIMEN"
20 PRINT "------------------------------------------------"
30 PRINT
40 PRINT "INPUT:"
50 PRINT "SPECIMEN THICKNESS B (MM)";
60 INPUT B
70 B=B/1000
```

Example 7.6 Fracture toughness test   117

```
80 PRINT "OVERALL SPECIMEN WIDTH - EQUALS 1.25*W - (MM)";
90 INPUT W
100 W=W/1.25
110 PRINT "DISTANCE FROM FATIGUE CRACK TIP TO CRACKED SIDE OF SPECIMEN (MM)";
120 INPUT A
130 A=A-.25*W
140 PRINT
150 PRINT "SPECIMEN DIMENSIONS:"
160 PRINT "LENGTH";1.2*W;"MM"
170 PRINT "HOLE DIAMETER";.25*W;"MM"
180 PRINT "DISTANCE BETWEEN HOLE CENTRES";.55*W;"MM"
190 PRINT "LARGEST WIDTH DIMENSION FROM HOLE CENTRES";W;"MM"
200 PRINT "* DOES YOUR SPECIMEN HAVE THESE CORRECT DIMENSIONS?"
210 PRINT
220 PRINT "CRACK LENGTH A IS";A;"MM ";
230 IF A>=.45*W THEN 260
240 PRINT "WHICH IS OUTSIDE THE LIMITS";.45*W;"TO";.55*W
250 STOP
260 IF A>.55*W THEN 240
270 PRINT "WHICH IS INSIDE THE LIMITS";.45*W;"TO";.55*W
280 PRINT
290 PRINT "TYPE 'YES' IF YOUR SPECIMEN IS SATISFACTORY,'NO' IF IT IS NOT";
300 INPUT A$
310 IF A$="YES" THEN 330
320 IF A$<>"NO" THEN 290
325 STOP
330 PRINT
340 A=A/1000
350 W=W/1000
360 PRINT "INPUT THE FAILURE LOAD P (KN)";
370 INPUT P
380 P=P/1000
390 PRINT "FOR THE TEST TO BE VALID THE MAXIMUM LOAD RECORDED MUST BE"
400 PRINT "LESS THAN";1100*P;"KN"
410 PRINT "INPUT THE MATERIAL YIELD STRENGTH (N/MM^2)";
420 INPUT Y
430 PRINT
440 C=A/W
450 K=29.6*SQR(C)-185.5*C^(3/2)+655.7*C^(5/2)-1017*C^(7/2)+638.9*C^(9/2)
460 K=K*P/B/SQR(W)
470 A1=2.5*(K/Y)^2
480 IF A>=A1 THEN 500
490 PRINT "THE TEST IS NOT VALID: A<";A1*1000;"MM"
500 B1=A1
510 IF B>=B1 THEN 530
520 PRINT "THE TEST IS NOT VALID: B<";B1*1000;"MM"
530 W1=2*A1
540 IF W>=W1 THEN 560
550 PRINT "THE TEST IS NOT VALID: W<";W1*1000;"MM"
560 PRINT
570 PRINT "FRACTURE TOUGHNESS K1C =";K;"MN/M^3/2"
580 PRINT "---------------------------------------------------"
590 PRINT
600 PRINT "TYPE 0(TO STOP), 1(FOR NEW TEST WITH DIFFERENT DIMENSIONS),"
610 PRINT "2(FOR NEW TEST WITH JUST MAXIMUM LOAD CHANGED)";
620 INPUT Z
630 PRINT
640 ON Z+1 THEN 650,80,360
650 STOP

READY

RUN

EX7POINT6 12-MAY-82  12:49:37

FRACTURE TOUGHNESS TEST: COMPACT TENSION SPECIMEN
--------------------------------------------------
INPUT:
SPECIMEN THICKNESS B (MM)? 25
OVERALL SPECIMEN WIDTH - EQUALS 1.25*W - (MM)? 100
DISTANCE FROM FATIGUE CRACK TIP TO CRACKED SIDE OF SPECIMEN (MM)? 60
```

```
SPECIMEN DIMENSIONS:
LENGTH 96 MM
HOLE DIAMETER 20 MM
DISTANCE BETWEEN HOLE CENTRES 44 MM
LARGEST WIDTH DIMENSION FROM HOLE CENTRES 80 MM
* DOES YOUR SPECIMEN HAVE THESE CORRECT DIMENSIONS?

CRACK LENGTH A IS 40 MM WHICH IS INSIDE THE LIMITS 36 TO 44

TYPE 'YES' IF YOUR SPECIMEN IS SATISFACTORY,'NO' IF IT IS NOT? YES

INPUT THE FAILURE LOAD P (KN)? 35
FOR THE TEST TO BE VALID THE MAXIMUM LOAD RECORDED MUST BE
LESS THAN 38.5 KN
INPUT THE MATERIAL YIELD STRENGTH (N/MM^2)? 700


FRACTURE TOUGHNESS K1C = 47.5344 MN/M^3/2
--------------------------------------------

TYPE 0(TO STOP), 1(FOR NEW TEST WITH DIFFERENT DIMENSIONS),
2(FOR NEW TEST WITH JUST MAXIMUM LOAD CHANGED)? 2

INPUT THE FAILURE LOAD P (KN)? 35
FOR THE TEST TO BE VALID THE MAXIMUM LOAD RECORDED MUST BE
LESS THAN 38.5 KN
INPUT THE MATERIAL YIELD STRENGTH (N/MM^2)? 300

THE TEST IS NOT VALID: A< 62.7643 MM
THE TEST IS NOT VALID: B< 62.7643 MM
THE TEST IS NOT VALID: W< 125.529 MM


FRACTURE TOUGHNESS K1C = 47.5344 MN/M^3/2
--------------------------------------------

TYPE 0(TO STOP), 1(FOR NEW TEST WITH DIFFERENT DIMENSIONS),
2(FOR NEW TEST WITH JUST MAXIMUM LOAD CHANGED)? 0

STOP AT LINE 650

READY
```

Program notes

(1) The geometric data are specified in mm but are converted to metres for purposes of calculation.

(2) Input of the overall specimen width and thickness enables all the specimen dimensions except crack length to be calculated. The user is invited to check the specimen dimensions (line 200) and the program calculates whether the crack length lies within the necessary limits (lines 220–270).

(3) The program accepts only YES or NO as valid replies to the question as to whether the specimen is satisfactory (lines 290–320).

(4) The fracture toughness (K) is calculated in lines 440–460 using Equation (7.19).

(5) Equations (7.20) to check the specimen validity are evaluated in lines 470–550. The material yield strength is input as Y in line 420.

PROBLEMS

(7. 1) Write a program to determine safety factors assuming yielding is governed by

(1) the maximum shear stress criterion (Tresca), or
(2) the maximum shear strain energy criterion (Von Mises)

from 'run-time' input of component stresses σ_x, σ_y and τ_{xy} and material yield strength.

The program should use the subroutines in Example 7.2 to determine the principal stresses σ_1, σ_2 and σ_3, print their values and then use them to determine the safety factors as in Example 7.1.

Test the program with data derived from the combined bending and torsion problem in Example 7.3.

(7. 2) Write a program to determine whether a component fails by yielding or by brittle fracture. Values of the parameters K_{IC}, Q and a should be specified by 'run-time' input and used in Equation (7.7) to determine the applied stress for brittle fracture. The program should compare this stress with the material yield strength in order to determine the mode of failure.

How does a component fail when it contains a crack length 5 mm with Q equal to 0.405 if it is made of a material with a yield strength of 1050 N/mm² (MN/m²) and a fracture toughness (K_{IC}) of 46 MNm$^{-3/2}$?

(7.3) Extend the shaft design program of Example 7.3 to use the preferred diameter sizes detailed in Example 3.3. The actual safety factor for this preferred size design should be printed.

Further extensions would allow the design of hollow shafts and the input of power transmission requirements relevant to a vehicle axle, for example. See Problems (4.6) and (4.8).

(7. 4) Consider the design of a solid circular shaft to resist combined torsion and axial loading. Equation (7.16) gives an expression for the maximum value of the component shear stress τ_{xy} in terms of the unknown shaft diameter (d) and the prescribed torque (T). From Equation (3.1) the uniform arial direct stress can be expressed as

$$\sigma_x = 4P/\pi d^2 \qquad (7.21)$$

where P is the prescribed axial force.

Equation (6.6) gives the maximum shear stress at any point on the surface of the shaft in terms of σ_x, τ_{xy} and σ_y (which is zero). This equation can therefore be solved to give the required shaft diameter for a prescribed value of maximum shear stress − the maximum shear stress yield criterion. As a direct solution of this equation is difficult, a more practicable approach is to use an iterative procedure based on that described in Example 6.1 (or that in Example 6.2).

Write a program to do this and show that for a maximum shear stress of 115 N/mm² a shaft with a diameter of 77.4 (say 80) mm is required to carry a torque of 10 kNm and an axial load of 100 kN.

(7.5) An alloy steel has a fatigue strength of 550 N/mm² for 10^4 alternating load cycles which reduces to a fatigue limit of 275 N/mm² after 10^6 cycles.

The annual load spectrum for a component made of this material is as follows.

Stress (N/mm²)	Cycles (in units of 10⁴ cycles)
400	.5
370	1.5
350	3
330	1
310	2
290	1
230	1.5
210	6

Use the cumulative fatigue damage program in Example 7.4 to show that the fatigue life of the component is about 2½ years.

(7.6) Modify the fracture toughness test program in Example 7.6 so that it can be used for the bending test specimen shown in Figure 7.11.

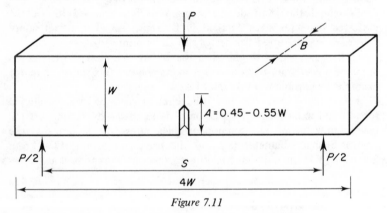

Figure 7.11

The fracture toughness (K_{IC}) for this specimen is given by

$$K_{IC} = \frac{P_Q S}{B W^{3/2}} \left[2.9 \left(\frac{a}{W}\right)^{1/2} - 4.6 \left(\frac{a}{W}\right)^{3/2} + 21.8 \left(\frac{a}{W}\right)^{5/2} \right.$$
$$\left. -37.6 \left(\frac{a}{W}\right)^{7/2} + 38.7 \left(\frac{a}{W}\right)^{9/2} \right]$$

$$(7.22)$$

The test procedure is similar to that described in Example 7.6 and the test validity conditions are identical.

(7. 7) Write a program to determine the effective length of columns with the end conditions shown in Figure 7.6. From 'run-time' input of support conditions at each end and actual column length the program should determine effective column lengths for use in Equations (7.13) and (7.14).

(7. 8) Modify the buckling program in Example 7.5 to include a wider range of cross-sections such as hollow square and rectangular.

A further modification would incorporate the procedure of Problem (7.7) so that the effective column length is determined automatically from specified end conditions.

(7.9) Study an empirical design procedure for buckling calculations from one of the references, page 13, or otherwise. Write a program based on one of these procedures in order to design a column.

(7. 10) The sections properties of T-, I- and L-shaped beams are determined in Example 5.4, Problem (5.7) and Problem (6.10) respectively. Their least second moments of area govern the buckling load capacity of columns in which they are incorporated. Introduce one or more of these sections to the program in Example 7.5.

(7. 11) A numerical procedure for evaluating Equation (7.11), which determines the number of cycles (N_1) for a fatigue crack to grow from length a_0 to a_1, is as follows

(1) divide the crack growth $(a_1 - a_0)$ into a number of equal increments of length δa,

(2) evaluate ΔK for crack length a_0 using Equation (7.9) with values of Q, σ_{max} and σ_{min} specified as data,

(3) evaluate da/dN for crack length a_0 using Equation (7.10) with values of C and m specified as data,

(4) repeat (2) and (3) for crack length $a_0 + \delta a$,

(5) evaluate the average value of da/dN over this increment of crack growth giving

$$\frac{d(a + \dfrac{\delta a}{2})}{dN} = \frac{1}{2}\left[\frac{da_0}{dN} + \frac{d(a_0 + \delta a)}{dN}\right] \qquad (7.23)$$

(6) hence obtain the number of cycles (δN) for this increment of crack growth where

$$\delta N = \frac{\delta a}{da/dN} = \frac{\delta a}{d(a + \frac{1}{2}\delta a)/dN} \qquad (7.24)$$

(7) repeat (2) to (6) for crack lengths $a_0 + 2\delta a, a_0 + 3\delta a$, etc., up

to a_1. Add the δN's to give the total number of cycles N_1 for the crack to grow from a_0 to a_1.

Write a program to follow this procedure and use it to show that about 77,000 loading cycles are required for the crack shown in Figure 7.12 to grow from 2 cm to 4 cm if σ_{max} = 60 MN/m^2, σ_{min} = 6 MN/m^2, Q = 1.2, C = 5 $\times$ 10^{-11} and m = 3.

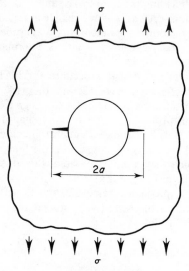

Figure 7.12

This particular problem can be solved by closed form analysis but for many problems Q, itself a function of crack length and a numerical prcoedure, is mandatory. This approach to fatigue crack propagation is discussed in Reference (7), page 13.

Chapter 8

Axisymmetric systems

ESSENTIAL THEORY

8.1 Introduction

Axisymmetric structures have geometrical symmetry about an axis and in addition have symmetry of loading about the same axis. Common examples are thin- and thick-walled, pressurised, cylindrical vessels and rotating discs.

8.2 Thin-walled cylindrical and spherical pressure vessels

Consider an internally pressurised cylindrical vessel with closed ends. If the wall thickness (t) is small compared with the cylinder diameter (d), it is reasonable to assume that any bending stresses and the direct stress in the *radial* direction (σ_r) are negligible. The cylinder walls have direct stress components in the direction of the *longitudinal* axis of the cylinder (σ_z) and in the circumferential direction around the cylinder (σ_θ). This latter stress is called a circumferential, tangentially or (most commonly) a *hoop* stress.

Values for these *biaxial* stress components are obtained by considering the equilibrium of parts of the cylinder for an internal pressure p. Hence

$$\sigma_z = pd/4t \tag{8.1}$$

and

$$\sigma_\theta = pd/2t \tag{8.2}$$

Because of symmetry, the longitudinal, circumferential and radial directions are on principal planes and it follows that σ_z, σ_θ and σ_r ($= 0$) are principal stresses.

A similar analysis for an internally pressurised thin-walled sphere of diameter d and wall thickness t gives a direct stress

$$\sigma = pd/4t \tag{8.3}$$

in all circumferential directions.

8.3 Pressurised thick-walled cylinders

Figure 8.1 shows the cross-section of a thick-walled cylindrical vessel that is subjected to an internal or an external pressure (or both). There

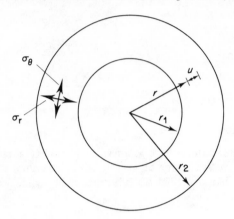

Figure 8.1

are radial (σ_r) and hoop (σ_θ) stresses which vary with radius r but are uniform in the direction of the longitudinal axis of the cylinder. The longitudinal stress (σ_z) is uniform. Suppose the radial displacement of any point at radius r is u as shown in Figure 8.1. At this radius there is

$$\text{a radial strain} \quad \epsilon_r = \frac{du}{dr} \tag{8.4}$$

and

$$\text{a hoop strain} \quad \epsilon_\theta = \frac{u}{r} \tag{8.5}$$

and in the longitudinal direction the strain (ϵ_z) is zero or constant depending on the end conditions.

The expressions for strain represent conditions of compatibility. An equilibrium condition can be obtained by considering the forces acting on a small element in the cross-section. Equations (3.4) with r replacing x and θ replacing y give the stress–strain relations assuming the material is isotropic and linearly elastic. When considered together, these conditions give the *Lamé* equations

$$\sigma_r = A - B/r^2 \tag{8.6}$$

$$\sigma_\theta = A + B/r^2 \tag{8.7}$$

The constants A and B are found from the boundary conditions to a particular problem.

The cylinder in Figure 8.1 has an internal radius r_1 (diameter d_1) and an external radius r_2 (diameter d_2). When subjected to an internal pressure p the boundary conditions are

$$\sigma_r = -p \text{ at } r = r_1$$

and

$$\sigma_r = 0 \text{ at } r = r_2$$

which, when substituted into Equation (8.6), give

$$A = \frac{r_1{}^2 p}{(r_2{}^2 - r_1{}^2)} \tag{8.8}$$

and

$$B = \frac{r_1{}^2 r_2{}^2 p}{(r_2{}^2 - r_1{}^2)} \tag{8.9}$$

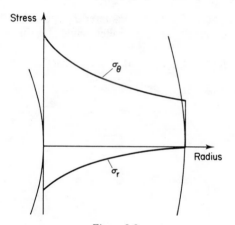

Figure 8.2

The distribution of σ_r and σ_θ across the wall thickness for an internally pressurised cylinder are shown in Figure 8.2. The maximum hoop stress occurs at the inside (bore) of the cylinder ($\sigma_{\theta 1}$ at radius r_1) and its value is found by substituting Equations (8.8) and (8.9) into Equations (8.7) with r equal to r_1. Hence

$$\sigma_{\theta 1} = \frac{r_1{}^2 p}{(r_2{}^2 - r_1{}^2)} \left(1 + \frac{r_2{}^2}{r_1{}^2}\right)$$

$$= \frac{(k^2 + 1)}{(k^2 - 1)} \cdot p \tag{8.10}$$

where

$$k = \frac{r_2}{r_1} = \frac{d_2}{d_1}$$

The hoop strain at any radius is obtained by combining Equation (8.5) with one of the Equations (3.4) to give

$$\epsilon_\theta = \frac{u}{r} = \frac{1}{E}(\sigma_\theta - \nu\sigma_r) \tag{8.11}$$

As can be seen from Figure 8.2, the stresses in an internally pressurised cylinder are much higher near its bore — it will yield there when the stresses towards the outside of the cylinder are still low. This inefficient utilisation of material is minimised by making a compound cylinder or by using autofrettage.

8.4 Compound cylinders

Suppose a cylinder of external diameter d_2 and internal diameter c is heated and then shrunk on to a smaller cylinder as shown in Figure 8.3. The smaller inner cylinder has an internal diameter d_1 and an external diameter which is nominally c but is larger than the internal diameter of

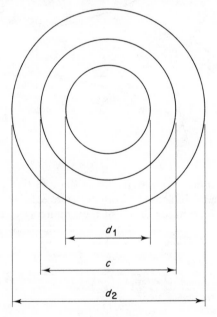

Figure 8.3

the outer cylinder by a small amount δ — the *interference* between the two cylinders.

After assembly there is a radial pressure p at the common diameter which reduces the hoop stresses in the inner cylinder. As a consequence there is a more uniform distribution of hoop stress upon subsequent internal pressurisation of the compound cylinder.

At the common diameter (c) the hoop strain

$$\epsilon_\theta = \epsilon_\theta{}^{\text{outer}} - \epsilon_\theta{}^{\text{inner}} \text{ at } r = c/2$$

$$= \delta/c \text{ from Equation (8.11)}$$

At the common diameter, therefore, substituting the hoop strains in each cylinder ($\epsilon_\theta{}^{\text{outer}}$ and $\epsilon_\theta{}^{\text{inner}}$) into the stress–strain relations from Equations (3.4) gives

$$\frac{\delta}{c} = \frac{1}{E}(\sigma_\theta{}^{\text{outer}} - \sigma_\theta{}^{\text{inner}}) \text{ at } r = c/2 \qquad (8.12)$$

assuming both cylinders are made of the same material with Young's modulus E.

The stress boundary conditions for the inner cylinder are

$$\sigma_r = 0 \text{ at } r = d_1/2$$

$$= -p \text{ at } r = c/2$$

and for the outer cylinder the boundary conditions are

$$\sigma_r = -p \text{ at } r = c/2$$

$$= 0 \text{ at } r = d_2/2$$

These can be substituted separately into Equation (8.6) for each cylinder to obtain A and B. Hence expressions for hoop stress in each cylinder at the common diameter can be substituted into Equation (8.11) to give

$$\frac{\delta E}{pc} = \frac{d_2{}^2 + c^2}{d_2{}^2 - c^2} + \frac{c^2 + d_1{}^2}{c^2 - d_1{}^2} \qquad (8.13)$$

For a known interference δ the interfacial radial pressure p can be found from this equation. Hence the stress distribution in the assembled compound cylinder can be calculated.

The stresses due to subsequent internal pressurisation can be determined by assuming the compound cylinder is a single cylinder of internal diameter d_1 and external diameter d_2 and then adding them to the initial residual stresses using the principle of superposition.

8.5 Autofrettage

This method for giving a beneficial residual stress distribution involves pressurising a single thick-walled cylinder until there is yielding of its inner layers. When the pressure is released these inner layers are put into compression supported by residual tensile stresses in the outer elastically deformed layers.

The Tresca yield criterion (Equation (7.2)) can be used to determine the pressure p necessary to cause yielding out to a radius r_Y. Thus

$$p = Y \ln \frac{r_Y}{r_1} + \frac{\sigma_Y}{2r_2^2} (r_2^2 - r_2^2 - r_Y^2) \tag{8.14}$$

where r_1 and r_2 are respectively the internal and external radii of the cylinder and σ_Y is the yield strength of a material which is assumed to be elastic – perfectly plastic as shown in Figure 8.4.

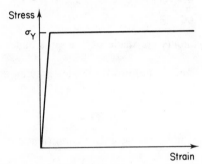

Figure 8.4

The residual stresses in the cylinder are found from superposition of the stresses due to initial pressurisation and the stresses due to the elastic unloading caused by removal of this pressure. Hence, for the region that has yielding $r_1 \leqslant r < r_Y$

$$\sigma_r = -p + \sigma_Y \ln \frac{r}{r_1} - \frac{pr_1^2}{r_2^2 - r_1^2} \left(1 - \frac{r_2^2}{r^2}\right)$$

$$\sigma_\theta = -p + \sigma_Y \left(1 + \ln \frac{r}{r_1}\right) - \frac{pr_1^2}{r_2^2 - r_1^2} \left(1 + \frac{r_2^2}{r^2}\right) \tag{8.15}$$

and for the elastic region $r_Y < r \leqslant r_2$

$$\sigma_r = \left[\frac{\sigma_Y r_Y^2}{2r_2^2} - \frac{pr_1^2}{r_2^2 - r_1^2}\right]\left[1 - \frac{r_2^2}{r^2}\right]$$

$$\sigma_\theta = \left[\frac{\sigma_Y r_Y^2}{2r_2^2} - \frac{pr_1^2}{r_2^2 - r_1^2}\right]\left[1 + \frac{r_2^2}{r^2}\right] \tag{8.16}$$

Example 8.1 Design of thin-walled pressure vessel 129

8.6 Rotating cylinders and discs

Consider a thin-walled cylinder of radius r and wall thickness t which rotates about its longitudinal axis with an angular velocity ω. Centrifugal force produces a hoop stress σ, the value of which can be found by considering the equilibrium of a small element of the wall. Hence

$$\sigma = \rho r^2 \omega^2 \qquad (8.17)$$

Consider a thin circular disc which rotates about its longitudinal axis with an angular velocity ω. Because it is thin in the longitudinal (z) direction the axial stress σ_z is zero. A similar procedure to that used for the analysis of stresses in thick-walled pressurised cylinders gives equations for the radial (σ_r) and hoop (σ_θ) stresses. Thus

$$\sigma_r = A - \frac{B}{r^2} - \frac{(3+\nu)}{8}\,\rho r^2 \omega^2$$
$$\sigma_\theta = A + \frac{B}{r^2} - \frac{(1+3\nu)}{8}\,\rho r^2 \omega^2 \qquad (8.18)$$

The constants are found from the boundary conditions.

For a solid disc the constant B is zero and A is found by evaluating $\sigma_r = 0$ at the outside radius.

For a hollow disc the constants are found from the conditions

$$\sigma_r = 0 \text{ at } r = r_2 \text{, the outside radius}$$

and

$$\sigma_r = 0 \text{ at } r = r_1 \text{, the inside radius.}$$

WORKED EXAMPLES

Example 8.1 Design of thin-walled pressure vessel

Write a program to design a thin-walled cylindrical vessel with closed ends to support a prescribed internal pressure. Use 'run-time' input to specify the maximum allowable tensile stress and required pressure. Then, for a specified diameter (d) or wall thickness (t) the program should determine the other dimension. The program should print a warning and stop if d/t is less than 20.

```
EX8POINT1  7-JUL-81  09:11:05

10 PRINT "DESIGN OF THIN-WALLED CYLINDRICAL PRESSURE VESSEL"
20 PRINT "_____"
30 PRINT
40 PRINT "INPUT:"
50 PRINT "MAX ALLOWABLE DIRECT STRESS (N/MM^2)";
60 INPUT S
70 PRINT "MAX INTERNAL PRESSURE (N/MM^2)";
80 INPUT P
90 PRINT
```

```
100 PRINT "DIAMETER OR WALL THICKNESS (MM) - INPUT 0 TO STOP"
110 PRINT "USE -VE VALUES TO PRESCRIBE WALL THICKNESS";
120 INPUT A
130 IF A<>0 THEN 150
140 STOP
150 IF A>0 THEN 200
160 T=-A
170 D=2*S*T/P
180 PRINT "REQUIRED DIAMETER";D;"MM"
185 GOSUB 500
190 GO TO 90
200 D=A
210 T=P*D/S/2
220 PRINT "REQUIRED WALL THICKNESS";T;"MM"
225 GOSUB 500
230 GO TO 90
500 REM SUBROUTINE TO CHECK VALIDITY OF 'THIN' CYLINDER FORMULA
510 PRINT "DIAMETER:WALL THICKNESS RATIO";D/T
520 IF D/T>=20 THEN 580
530 IF D/T>2 THEN 560
540 PRINT "DESIGN IMPRACTICAL - DIMENSIONS IMPOSSIBLE!"
550 STOP
560 PRINT "THE DESIGN SHOULD BE BASED ON 'THICK' CYLINDER THEORY"
570 STOP
580 RETURN

READY

RUN

EX8POINT1   7-JUL-81   09:11:56

DESIGN OF THIN-WALLED CYLINDRICAL PRESSURE VESSEL
----------------------------------------------------

INPUT:
MAX ALLOWABLE DIRECT STRESS (N/MM^2)? 100
MAX INTERNAL PRESSURE (N/MM^2)? 5

DIAMETER OR WALL THICKNESS (MM) - INPUT 0 TO STOP
USE -VE VALUES TO PRESCRIBE WALL THICKNESS? 500
REQUIRED WALL THICKNESS 12.5 MM
DIAMETER:WALL THICKNESS RATIO 40

DIAMETER OR WALL THICKNESS (MM) - INPUT 0 TO STOP
USE -VE VALUES TO PRESCRIBE WALL THICKNESS? -10
REQUIRED DIAMETER 400 MM
DIAMETER:WALL THICKNESS RATIO 40

DIAMETER OR WALL THICKNESS (MM) - INPUT 0 TO STOP
USE -VE VALUES TO PRESCRIBE WALL THICKNESS? 0

STOP AT LINE 140

READY
```

Program notes

(1) The maximum direct stress in a thin-walled cylindrical vessel is the circumferential hoop stress given by Equation (8.2). This equation is evaluated in lines 170 and 210 to determine the diameter (D) or thickness (T) respectively.

(2) The value of A specified in line 120 indicates by its sign whether the diameter or wall thickness is prescribed. It is converted to either a

Example 8.2 Vessel design for torsion and internal pressure   131

diameter in line 200 or, with a change of sign, to a wall thickness in line 160.

(3) The subroutine (lines 500 to 580) is used to check that the ratio of diameter to wall thickness is not too small for thin cylinder theory to apply (see Problem (8.1)). It is clearly impossible to have a ratio of D/T less than 2.

Example 8.2 Vessel design for torsion and internal pressure

Write a program to design a thin-walled cylindrical vessel subjected to torsion and internal pressure using 'run-time' input to specify the torque (in kNm) and the internal pressure (in N/mm^2). Then, for a specified external diameter (in mm) determine the maximum shear stress for specified values of wall thickness (in mm). Iterate the wall thickness until the shear stress is near to a known allowable value. The program should print a warning if the ratio of diameter to wall thickness is less than 20.

Use the program to design a vessel to withstand a torque of 20 kNm and an internal pressure of 5 N/mm^2 if the maximum shear stress should not exceed 50 N/mm^2.

```
EX8POINT2   7-JUL-81   09:15:52

10 PRINT "ITERATIVE DESIGN OF THIN-WALLED CYLINDRICAL VESSEL"
20 PRINT "SUBJECT TO TORSION AND INTERNAL PRESSURE"
30 PRINT "----------------------------------------------------------"
40 PRINT
50 PRINT "INPUT:"
60 PRINT "MAX TORQUE (KNM)";
70 INPUT T0
80 T0=T0*1.00000E+06
90 PRINT "MAX INTERNAL PRESSURE (N/MM^2)";
100 INPUT P
110 PRINT
120 PRINT "DESIRED EXTERNAL DIAMETER (MM)";
130 INPUT D2
140 PRINT
150 PRINT "INPUT WALL THICKNESSES UNTIL MAX ALLOWABLE SHEAR STRESS"
160 PRINT "IS ACHIEVED (0 TO STOP, -VE VALUE TO CHANGE DIAMETER)"
170 PRINT
180 PRINT "WALL THICKNESS (MM)";
190 INPUT T
200 IF T<0 THEN 110
210 IF T>0 THEN 230
220 STOP
230 IF D2/T>=20 THEN 270
240 PRINT "DIAMETER:WALL THICKNESS RATIO =";D2/T;"  AS THIS"
250 PRINT "IS LESS THAN 20 'THIN' CYLINDER THEORY IS NOT APPLICABLE"
260 GO TO 170
270 D1=D2-2*T
280 X9=P*D1/4/T
290 Y9=P*D1/2/T
300 T9=16*T0*D2/(3.14159*(D2^4-D1^4))
310 GOSUB 1000
320 PRINT "MAX SHEAR STRESS";(S1-S3)/2;"N/MM^2"
330 GO TO 170
1000 REM SUBROUTINE TO DETERMINE 2D PRINCIPAL STRESSES (P1,P2)
1010 REM FROM COMPONENT STRESSES SIGX (X9), SIGY (Y9) AND TAUXY (T9)
```

```
1020 REM AND TO SORT THEM INTO 3D PRINCIPAL STRESSES (S1,S2,S3)
1030 P1=(Y9+X9)/2+SQR(((Y9-X9)/2)^2+T9*T9)
1040 P2=(Y9+X9)/2-SQR(((Y9-X9)/2)^2+T9*T9)
1050 IF P1>0 THEN 1100
1060 S1=0
1070 S2=P1
1080 S3=P2
1090 GO TO 1170
1100 S1=P1
1110 IF P2<0 THEN 1150
1120 S2=P2
1130 S3=0
1140 GO TO 1170
1150 S2=0
1160 S3=P2
1170 RETURN

READY


RUN


EX8POINT2   7-JUL-81   09:16:56

ITERATIVE DESIGN OF THIN-WALLED CYLINDRICAL VESSEL
SUBJECT TO TORSION AND INTERNAL PRESSURE
-------------------------------------------------------

INPUT:
MAX TORQUE (KNM)? 20
MAX INTERNAL PRESSURE (N/MM^2)? 5

DESIRED EXTERNAL DIAMETER (MM)? 300

INPUT WALL THICKNESSES UNTIL MAX ALLOWABLE SHEAR STRESS
IS ACHIEVED (0 TO STOP, -VE VALUE TO CHANGE DIAMETER)

WALL THICKNESS (MM)? 1
MAX SHEAR STRESS 396.75 N/MM^2

WALL THICKNESS (MM)? 5
MAX SHEAR STRESS 77.8221 N/MM^2

WALL THICKNESS (MM)? 7
MAX SHEAR STRESS 55.0528 N/MM^2

WALL THICKNESS (MM)? 8
MAX SHEAR STRESS 47.94 N/MM^2

WALL THICKNESS (MM)? 7.7
MAX SHEAR STRESS 49.8797 N/MM^2

WALL THICKNESS (MM)? -1

DESIRED EXTERNAL DIAMETER (MM)? 400

INPUT WALL THICKNESSES UNTIL MAX ALLOWABLE SHEAR STRESS
IS ACHIEVED (0 TO STOP, -VE VALUE TO CHANGE DIAMETER)

WALL THICKNESS (MM)? 5
MAX SHEAR STRESS 98.8623 N/MM^2

WALL THICKNESS (MM)? 10
MAX SHEAR STRESS 48.2512 N/MM^2

WALL THICKNESS (MM)? 0

STOP AT LINE 220

READY
```

Example 8.3 Thick cylinder stress distribution   133

Program notes

(1) In line 270 the internal diameter D1 is determined from the external diameter D2 and the wall thickness T.

(2) The component stresses for any point in the (thin) wall are determined in lines 280 to 300. X9 is the longitudinal direct stress (σ_x) from Equation (8.1). Y9 is the circumferential hoop stress (σ_y) from Equation (8.2). T9 is the shear stress (τ_{xy}) obtained from Equations (4.7) and (4.10).

(3) The principal stresses (S1, S2 and S3) are calculated from these component stresses in the subroutine (lines 1000 to 1170) which combines the two subroutines in Example 7.2. The principal stresses are used to determine the maximum shear stress in line 320.

(4) The program takes no account of torsional buckling which is possible for very thin-walled vessels.

Example 8.3 Thick cylinder stress distribution

Write a program to tabulate the distribution of radial and hoop stress in an internally pressurised thick-walled cylinder. The program should use 'run-time' input of internal and external radii (in mm), internal pressure (in N/mm²) and the number of positions for which output is required. Plot a stress distribution and compare with that shown in Figure 8.2.

```
EX8POINT3   7-JUL-81   09:19:27

10 PRINT "STRESS DISTRIBUTION IN AN INTERNALLY"
20 PRINT "PRESSURISED THICK-WALLED CYLINDER"
30 PRINT "_____-"
40 PRINT
50 PRINT "INPUT:"
60 PRINT "INTERNAL RADIUS (MM)";
70 INPUT R1
80 PRINT "EXTERNAL RADIUS (MM)";
90 INPUT R2
100 PRINT "INTERNAL PRESSURE (N/MM^2)";
110 INPUT P
120 A=P*R1^2/(R2^2-R1^2)
130 B=P*R1^2*R2^2/(R2^2-R1^2)
140 PRINT
150 PRINT "NUMBER OF POSITIONS FOR WHICH STRESS"
160 PRINT "OUTPUT REQUIRED (1 OR LESS TO STOP)";
170 INPUT N
180 IF N>1 THEN 200
190 STOP
200 PRINT
210 PRINT "RADIUS","HOOP STRESS","RADIAL STRESS"
220 PRINT "  (MM)","  (N/MM^2)","   (N/MM^2)"
230 FOR I=0 TO N-1
240 R=R1+I*(R2-R1)/(N-1)
250 S1=A+B/R^2
260 S3=A-B/R^2
270 PRINT R,S1,S3
280 NEXT I
290 GO TO 140

READY
```

```
RUN

EX8POINT3   7-JUL-81   09:20:09

STRESS DISTRIBUTION IN AN INTERNALLY
PRESSURISED THICK-WALLED CYLINDER
---------------------------------------------

INPUT:
INTERNAL RADIUS (MM)? 75
EXTERNAL RADIUS (MM)? 105
INTERNAL PRESSURE (N/MM^2)? 40

NUMBER OF POSITIONS FOR WHICH STRESS
OUTPUT REQUIRED (1 OR LESS TO STOP)? 2

RADIUS        HOOP STRESS    RADIAL STRESS
 (MM)          (N/MM^2)        (N/MM^2)
 75            123.333        -40
 105           83.3333        3.81470E-06

NUMBER OF POSITIONS FOR WHICH STRESS
OUTPUT REQUIRED (1 OR LESS TO STOP)? 7

RADIUS        HOOP STRESS    RADIAL STRESS
 (MM)          (N/MM^2)        (N/MM^2)
 75            123.333        -40
 80            113.444        -30.1107
 85            105.248        -21.9146
 90            98.3796        -15.0463
 95            92.5669        -9.2336
 100           87.6042        -4.27083
 105           83.3333        3.81470E-06

NUMBER OF POSITIONS FOR WHICH STRESS
OUTPUT REQUIRED (1 OR LESS TO STOP)? 0

STOP AT LINE 190

READY
```

Program notes

(1) The constants A and B are determined in lines 120 and 130 using Equations (8.8) and (8.9) respectively.

(2) The variable I in the loop (lines 230 to 280) is used to calculate each radius (R) in line 240. The number of positions (N) must be at least two to prevent (N − 1) being zero or negative in line 240.

(3) The hoop stress (S1) and the radial stress (S3) are calculated from the Lamé Equations (8.6) and (8.7) in lines 250 and 260.

Example 8.4 Experimental thick cylinder measurements

Consider a thick-walled tube of known dimensions (external diameter D_2, internal diameter D_1) and material properties (Young's modulus E and Poisson's ratio v). Suppose the tube is subjected to a particular but unmeasured internal pressure (p). It is possible to determine this pressure, the maximum shear stress (at the bore) and the increase in

Example 8.4 Experimental thick cylinder measurements 135

internal diameter (δ_1) from a measurement of just the increase in external diameter (δ_2).

Write a program to evaluate the results of such an experiment having verified Equations (8.19), (8.20) and (8.21), the derivation of which is indicated below.

Equations (8.8) and (8.9) can be substituted into Equations (8.6) and (8.7) to enable σ_r and σ_θ to be evaluated at the outside diameter (D_2). Substitution of these stress expressions into Equation (8.11) for the outside diameter (D_2) where $\epsilon_\theta = \delta_2/D_2$ gives an expression for the internal pressure (p) in terms of known parameters, i.e.

$$p = \frac{\delta_2 E(D_2{}^2 - D_1{}^2)}{2D_2 D_1{}^2} \tag{8.19}$$

The maximum shear stress (τ_{max}) occurs at the bore where

$$\tau_{max} = \frac{\sigma_\theta - \sigma_r}{2} = \frac{pD_2{}^2}{(D_2{}^2 - D_1{}^2)} = \frac{\delta_2 E D_2}{2D_1{}^2} \tag{8.20}$$

Substituting expressions for σ_θ and σ_r into Equation (8.11) for the bore where the diameter is D_1 and $\epsilon_\theta = \delta_1/D_1$ gives an expression for the increase in internal diameter

$$\delta_1 = \frac{\delta_2}{2D_1 D_2} (D_1{}^2 (1 - \nu) + D_2{}^2 (1 + \nu)) \tag{8.21}$$

```
EX8POINT4   7-JUL-81   09:24:23

10 PRINT "PRESSURISED THICK-WALLED TUBE PARAMETERS FROM"
20 PRINT "MEASUREMENTS OF INCREASE IN EXTERNAL DIAMETER"
30 PRINT "--------------------------------------------------"
40 PRINT
50 PRINT "INPUT:"
60 PRINT "YOUNG'S MODULUS (KN/MM^2)";
70 INPUT E
80 E=E*1000
90 PRINT "POISSON'S RATIO";
100 INPUT U
110 PRINT "EXTERNAL DIAMETER (MM)";
120 INPUT D2
130 PRINT "INTERNAL DIAMETER (MM)";
140 INPUT D1
150 PRINT
160 PRINT "INCREASE IN EXTERNAL DIAMETER (MM) - 0 TO STOP";
170 INPUT I2
180 IF I2>0 THEN 200
190 STOP
200 P=I2*E*(D2*D2-D1*D1)/(2*D2*D1*D1)
210 S=I2*E*D2/(2*D1*D1)
220 I1=I2*(D1*D1*(1-U)+D2*D2*(1+U))/(2*D1*D2)
230 PRINT "INTERNAL PRESSURE";P;"N/MM^2"
240 PRINT "MAX SHEAR STRESS AT BORE";S;"N/MM^2"
250 PRINT "INCREASE IN INTERNAL DIAMETER";I1;"MM"
260 GO TO 150

READY
```

```
RUN

EX8POINT4   7-JUL-81   09:25:09

PRESSURISED THICK-WALLED TUBE PARAMETERS FROM
MEASUREMENTS OF INCREASE IN EXTERNAL DIAMETER
--------------------------------------------------

INPUT:
YOUNG'S MODULUS (KN/MM^2)? 207
POISSON'S RATIO? .29
EXTERNAL DIAMETER (MM)? 210
INTERNAL DIAMETER (MM)? 150

INCREASE IN EXTERNAL DIAMETER (MM) - 0 TO STOP? .01
INTERNAL PRESSURE 4.73143 N/MM^2
MAX SHEAR STRESS AT BORE 9.66 N/MM^2
INCREASE IN INTERNAL DIAMETER .0115657 MM

INCREASE IN EXTERNAL DIAMETER (MM) - 0 TO STOP? .05
INTERNAL PRESSURE 23.6571 N/MM^2
MAX SHEAR STRESS AT BORE 48.3 N/MM^2
INCREASE IN INTERNAL DIAMETER .0578286 MM

INCREASE IN EXTERNAL DIAMETER (MM) - 0 TO STOP? .09
INTERNAL PRESSURE 42.5829 N/MM^2
MAX SHEAR STRESS AT BORE 86.94 N/MM^2
INCREASE IN INTERNAL DIAMETER .104091 MM

INCREASE IN EXTERNAL DIAMETER (MM) - 0 TO STOP? 0

STOP AT LINE 190

READY
```

Program notes

(1) The increase in external diameter δ_2 is represented by I2. The increase in internal diameter δ_1 is represented by I1.
(2) Equations (8.19), (8.20) and (8.21) are evaluated respectively in lines 200, 210 and 220.

Example 8.5 Stress distribution in a compound cylinder

Write a program to tabulate the residual distribution of radial and hoop stress in a compound cylinder after it has been assembled with a known interference at the common diameter. Assume the two cylinders are made of the same material and use 'run-time' input to specify Young's modulus of this material, the interference, the internal diameter of the inner cylinder, the external diameter of the outer cylinder and the common cylinder diameter. 'Run-time' input should also be used to specify the number of positions through the wall thickness for which output is required. The stresses in both inner and outer cylinders at their common diameter should be printed whatever number of positions are specified.

Example 8.5 Stress distribution in a compound cylinder   137

```
EX8POINT5  7-JUL-81  09:28:37

10 PRINT "STRESS DISTRIBUTION IN A COMPOUND CYLINDER"
20 PRINT "------------------------------------------------"
30 PRINT
40 PRINT "INPUT:"
50 PRINT "YOUNG'S MODULUS (KN/MM^2)";
60 INPUT E
70 E=E*1000
80 PRINT "INTERNAL DIAMETER OF INNER CYLINDER (MM)";
90 INPUT D1
100 PRINT "EXTERNAL DIAMETER OF INNER CYLINDER (MM)";
110 INPUT C
120 PRINT "EXTERNAL DIAMETER OF OUTER CYLINDER (MM)";
130 INPUT D2
140 PRINT
150 PRINT "INTERFERENCE AT COMMON DIAMETER (MM)";
160 INPUT I
170 P=E*I/C/((D2^2+C^2)/(D2^2-C^2)+(C^2+D1^2)/(C^2-D1^2))
180 PRINT
190 PRINT "RADIAL PRESSURE AT COMMON DIAMETER";P;"N/MM^2"
200 PRINT
210 PRINT "NUMBER OF POSITIONS FOR OUTPUT OF RESIDUAL"
220 PRINT "STRESSES (1 OR LESS TO STOP)";
230 INPUT N
240 IF N>1 THEN 260
250 STOP
260 PRINT
270 PRINT "RADIUS","HOOP STRESS","RADIAL STRESS","CYLINDER"
280 PRINT " (MM)"," (N/MM^2)","  (N/MM^2)"
290 J1=0
300 FOR J=0 TO N-1
310 R=D1/2+J*(D2-D1)/2/(N-1)
320 IF R>=C/2 THEN 350
330 GOSUB 1000
340 GO TO 430
350 IF J1<>0 THEN 420
360 R1=R
370 R=C/2
380 GOSUB 1000
390 GOSUB 2000
400 J1=1
410 R=R1
420 GOSUB 2000
430 NEXT J
440 GO TO 200
1000 REM SUBROUTINE TO FIND RESIDUAL STRESSES IN INNER CYLINDER
1010 A=-P*C^2/(C^2-D1^2)
1020 B=-P*D1^2*C^2/4/(C^2-D1^2)
1030 PRINT R,A+B/R^2,A-B/R^2,"INNER"
1040 RETURN
2000 REM SUBROUTINE TO FIND RESIDUAL STRESSES IN OUTER CYLINDER
2010 A=P*C^2/(D2^2-C^2)
2020 B=P*C^2*D2^2/4/(D2^2-C^2)
2030 PRINT R,A+B/R^2,A-B/R^2,"OUTER"
2040 RETURN

READY

RUN

EX8POINT5  7-JUL-81  09:29:41

STRESS DISTRIBUTION IN A COMPOUND CYLINDER
------------------------------------------------
INPUT:
YOUNG'S MODULUS (KN/MM^2)? 207
INTERNAL DIAMETER OF INNER CYLINDER (MM)? 150
EXTERNAL DIAMETER OF INNER CYLINDER (MM)? 185
EXTERNAL DIAMETER OF OUTER CYLINDER (MM)? 210
```

```
INTERFERENCE AT COMMON DIAMETER (MM)? .05

RADIAL PRESSURE AT COMMON DIAMETER 4.38118 N/MM^2

NUMBER OF POSITIONS FOR OUTPUT OF RESIDUAL
STRESSES (1 OR LESS TO STOP)? 7

RADIUS          HOOP STRESS     RADIAL STRESS CYLINDER
 (MM)            (N/MM^2)         (N/MM^2)
  75             -25.5771         9.53674E-07    INNER
  80             -24.0285        -1.54862        INNER
  85             -22.7451        -2.83207        INNER
  90             -21.6695        -3.90762        INNER
  92.5           -21.196         -4.38118        INNER
  92.5            34.75          -4.38118        OUTER
  95              33.7338        -3.36496        OUTER
 100              31.9252        -1.5564         OUTER
 105              30.3688         0              OUTER

NUMBER OF POSITIONS FOR OUTPUT OF RESIDUAL
STRESSES (1 OR LESS TO STOP)? 0

STOP AT LINE 250

READY
```

Program notes

(1) The interfacial radial pressure at the common diameter (C) is determined as P in line 170 using Equation (8.13).

(2) After each radius (R) is calculated in line 310, a check is made in line 320 to identify whether it refers to the inner or outer cylinder.

When the outer cylinder is first referenced the variable J1 is zero as set in line 290 and lines 360 to 410 are executed. The radius R is temporarily stored as R1 (line 360) and the value of the common diameter (C/2) is used to determine stresses in both the inner and outer cylinders. The radius is then reset to its previous value (line 410). These lines are not reached for subsequent radii because J2 is set to 1 in line 400.

(3) The stresses in the outer cylinder are determined in a subroutine (lines 2000 to 2040). The outer cylinder is internally pressurised by the pressure P. The expressions for the constants A and B are those in Equations (8.8) and (8.9) but with diameters instead of radii. The stresses are then calculated and printed in a single statement (line 2030) using Equations (8.6) and (8.7).

(4) The stresses in the inner cylinder are determined in the subroutine from lines 1000 to 1040. The inner cylinder is externally pressurised by the pressure P. The expressions for the constants A and B in lines 1010 and 1020 are derived from Equation (8.6) using the boundary conditions

$$\sigma_r = 0 \text{ at } r = D1/2$$
$$= -P \text{ at } r = C/2$$

The stresses are then calculated and printed in line 1030 using Equations (8.6) and (8.7).

PROBLEMS

(8.1) Write a program to investigate the errors introduced by using the 'thin cylinder' formula, Equation (8.2), instead of the 'thick cylinder' formula, Equation (8.10), in order to predict the maximum hoop stress in an internally pressurised cylinder. Consider ratios of outside diameter to wall thickness from 5 to 100 and investigate whether it is better to use an internal, external or mean diameter in the 'thin cylinder' formula.

(8.2) Write a program to design spherical steel containers. The following data should be built into the program

(1) maximum allowable direct stress: 150 N/mm^2,
(2) available wall thicknesses: 1, 2, 5, 10, 20 mm.

The only 'run-time' input to the program should be the number of moles of gas (M) to be contained. The program should 'offer' the user a range of containers, their size (diameter) being governed by the wall thickness. The pressure at which the gas is stored should also be printed. Note: the gas pressure (p in N/mm^2) is related to its volume (V in mm^3) and the number of moles (M) by the equation

$$p = M/V \times 2.27 \times 10^6 \tag{8.22}$$

Equations (8.22) and (8.3) with an expression for the volume of a sphere in terms of its diameter enables the unknown diameter to be calculated for each wall thickness.

(8.3) Modify the program in Example 8.1 so that it selects from a range of preferred sizes for both wall thickness and diameter. A limited range of possible sizes for wall thickness are 1, 2, 3, 4, 5, 6, 8 and 10 mm and for diameter are 100, 200, 300, 400, 500, 600, 800 and 1000 mm. The program should print the actual maximum direct stress in the cylinder wall.

(8.4) Write a program to tabulate the distribution of radial and hoop stress in an *externally* pressurised thick-walled cylinder. The style of the program should be similar to that in Example 8.3. Run the program with the same data as is used in Example 8.3 and compare the two stress distributions.

(8.5) Extend the programs in Example 8.3 and Problem (8.4) to print the radial deformation (u) at each value of radius using Equation (8.11). Build into the program the properties (i.e. E and ν) of steel.

(8.6) An internally pressurised thick-walled cylinder first yields at the internal diameter where σ_r equals $-p$ and σ_θ is given by Equation (8.10). By substituting these stresses into the Tresca yield criterion (Equation (7.2)) show that the following relationship exists

$$k = \sqrt{\left(\frac{\delta_Y}{2p - \sigma_Y}\right)} \tag{8.23}$$

where k is the ratio of external to internal diameter and σ_Y is the material yield strength.

Use Equation (8.23) in a program to design an internally pressurised thick-walled pressure vessel against first yield. Use 'run-time' input to specify the material yield strength (in N/mm^2), a safety factor and the maximum internal pressure (in N/mm^2). The program should determine the other dimensions from a specified value of internal diameter, external diameter or wall thickness.

(8.7) Extend the program in Example 8.5 in order to determine the distribution of radial and hoop stress in a pressurised compound cylinder.

The program should determine the initial residual stresses as in Example 8.5 and then use 'run-time' input of subsequent internal pressurisation to calculate the additional stresses using Equations (8.6) to (8.9). The final stress distribution is obtained by superposition of the two stress systems.

(8.8) Write a program to tabulate the distribution of radial and hoop stress in a thick-walled cylinder after it has been autofrettaged as described in Section 8.5.

The program can be based on that in Example 8.5 except that the inner and outer cylinders are replaced by a plastic 'cylinder' surrounded by an elastic 'cylinder'. The internal and external cylinder radii (or diameters), the yield radius (r_Y) and the material yield strength should be specified by 'run-time' input.

The program could be extended for subsequent pressurisation as described in Problem (8.7).

(8.9) The rotating cylinder, Equation (8.17), can be used for the appropriate design of a flywheel with its mass concentrated in a heavy outside rim.

Use the following procedure to write a program for the design of such a flywheel.

For specified values of maximum allowable direct stress, material density and rotational speed (ω) Equation (8.17) gives the required outside radius. If the moment of inertia and rim width are also specified the rim thickness (i.e. the radial thickness) can be determined iteratively. An iterative approach is necessary because moment of inertia equals rim volume (a function of rim thickness and mean radius) multiplied by density multiplied by the square of the radius of gyration (also a function of rim thickness). The calculated outside radius can be used as a first estimate of mean radius to obtain a value of rim thickness. This thickness can then be used to make a better estimate of mean radius and radius of gyration. These calculations are repeated until the value of rim thickness changes between successive iterations by less than some specified tolerance.

Use the program to show that a rim thickness of about 63 mm is required for a flywheel of rim density 7200 kg/m^3, moment of inertia 250 kgm^2 and width 125 mm which operates at 250 rev/min with a maximum stress of 4 N/mm^2.

(8.10) Use the necessary boundary conditions to obtain Equations (8.18) for the stresses in thin rotating discs. Use these equations in a program to determine the stress distribution in any solid or hollow disc for which the dimensions, speed and material properties are specified.

Index